Grade 4-5
Summer Activity Playground

12 weeks of Summer Activities:

- → Math
- → ELA
- → Science
- → Reading
- → Social Studies

BRAIN HUNTER

Brain Hunter Prep is a division of ArgoPrep dedicated to providing high-quality workbooks for K-8th grade students. We have been awarded multiple awards for our curriculum, books and/or online program. Here are a few of our awards!

Our goal is to make your life easier, so let us know how we can help you by e-mailing us at: info@argoprep.com.

ISBN: 9781951048211
Published by Brain Hunter Prep.

Aknowlegments:
Icons made by Freepik, Creaticca Creative Agency, Pixel perfect , Pixel Buddha, Smashicons, Twitter , Good Ware, Smalllikeart, Nikita Golubev, monkik, DinosoftLabs, Icon Pond from www.flaticon.com

- ArgoPrep is a recipient of the prestigious **Mom's Choice Award.**
- ArgoPrep also received the 2019 **Seal of Approval** from Homeschool.com for our award-winning workbooks.
- ArgoPrep was awarded the 2019 **National Parenting Products Award, Gold Medal Parent's Choice Award** and a **Brain Child Award**

Want an amazing offer from ArgoPrep?

7 DAY ACCESS
to our online premium content at **www.argoprep.com**

Online premium content includes practice quizzes and drills with video explanations and an automatic grading system.

Chat with us live at **www.argoprep.com** for this exclusive offer.

Summer Activity Playground Series

Kindergarten
Summer Activity Playground

12 weeks of Summer Activities:

→ Math → Science
→ ELA → Reading
→ Social Studies

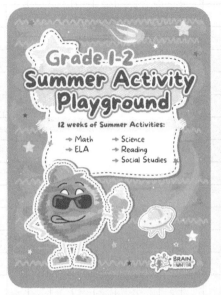

Grade 1-2
Summer Activity Playground

12 weeks of Summer Activities:

→ Math → Science
→ ELA → Reading
→ Social Studies

Grade 2-3
Summer Activity Playground

12 weeks of Summer Activities:

→ Math → Science
→ ELA → Reading
→ Social Studies

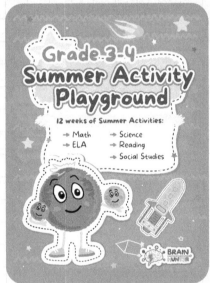

Grade 3-4
Summer Activity Playground

12 weeks of Summer Activities:

→ Math → Science
→ ELA → Reading
→ Social Studies

Grade 4-5
Summer Activity Playground

12 weeks of Summer Activities:

→ Math → Science
→ ELA → Reading
→ Social Studies

Grade 5-6
Summer Activity Playground

12 weeks of Summer Activities:

→ Math → Science
→ ELA → Reading
→ Social Studies

Grade 6-7
Summer Activity Playground

12 weeks of Summer Activities:

→ Math → Science
→ ELA → Reading
→ Social Studies

Grade 7-8
Summer Activity Playground

12 weeks of Summer Activities:

→ Math → Science
→ ELA → Reading
→ Social Studies

How to use this book?

Welcome to **Summer Activity Playground by Brain Hunter Prep!**

This workbook is specifically designed to prepare students over the summer to get ready for **Grade 5**. Our workbook is divided into twelve weeks so students can complete the entire workbook over the summer.

Our workbooks have been carefully designed and crafted by licensed teachers to give students an incredible learning experience. Students will be able to practice mathematics, english activities, science experiments, social studies, and fitness activities. Give your child the education they deserve!

Summer list to read

We strongly encourage students to read several books throughout the summer. Below you will find a recommended summer reading list that we have compiled for students entering into Grade 5. You can see this list at: www.argoprep.com/**summerlist**

Author: Gary Paulsen
Title: Hatchet

Author: Roland Smith
Title: Peak

Author: Frances Hodgson Burnett
Title: The Secret Garden

Author: Louis Sachar
Title: Holes

Author: Gary Paulsen
Title: Hatchet

Author: R.J. Palacio
Title: Wonder

Author: Katherine Paterson
Title: Bridge to Terabithia

Author: Lois Lowry
Title: The Giver

Author: Heather Lang
Title: Swimming with Sharks: The Daring Discoveries of Eugenie Clark

Author: Blue Balliett
Title: Chasing Vermeer

Author: Gary Paulsen
Title: Hatchet

OTHER BOOKS BY ARGOPREP

Here are some other test prep workbooks by ArgoPrep you may be interested in. All of our workbooks come equipped with detailed video explanations to make your learning experience a breeze! Visit us at **www.argoprep.com**

COMMON CORE MATH SERIES

  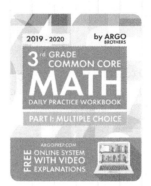 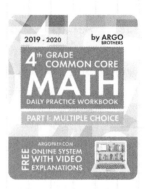

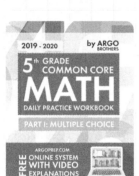 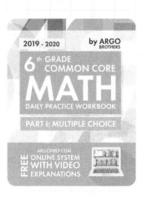 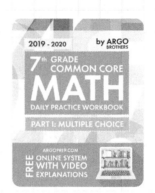 

COMMON CORE ELA SERIES

 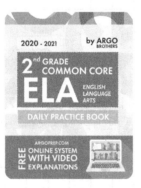 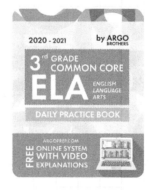 

 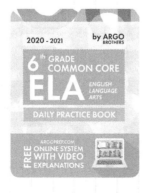  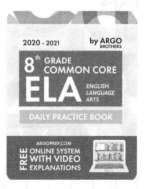

INTRODUCING MATH!

Introducing Math! by ArgoPrep is an award-winning series created by certified teachers to provide students with high-quality practice problems. Our workbooks include topic overviews with instruction, practice questions, answer explanations along with digital access to video explanations. Practice in confidence - with ArgoPrep!

  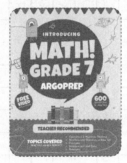 

YOGA
MINDFULNESS
FOR KIDS

HIGHER LEVEL EXAMS

WORKBOOKS INCLUDED

Comprehensive K-8 Math & ELA Program

www.argoprep.com/k8

Math & ELA success begins here

Real Results, Close Learning Gaps, Boost Confidence

30,000+
Practice Questions

500+
Video Lectures

15,000+
of Video Explanations

Printable
Worksheets, Games and more

Common Core
Next Generation Learning Standards & State Aligned

Grade 4-5
WEEK 1

Let's get started on:

* numbers and operations
* informational texts
* motion
* parts of a paragraph and more!

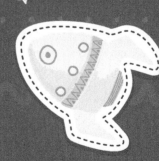

1. 35 = 7 x 5 is 7 times as much as 5.

....

....

2. 9 = 3 x 3 is 3 times as much as 3.

....

....

3. 90 = 10 x 9. is 10 times as much as 9.

....

....

4. 32 is times as much as 4.

....

....

5.  is 2 times as much as 4.

....

....

6. 12 is 2 times as much as .

....

....

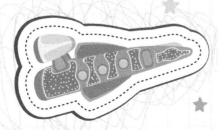

1. Julie sold boxes of chocolate to her neighbors. She sold **6** boxes on Saturday. She sold **3** times as many boxes on Sunday as she did on Saturday. How many boxes of chocolate did Julie sell on Sunday?

2. The Blue Ridge bike path is 1 mile long. The Cedar Hill bike path is **7** times as long as the Blue Ridge path. How many miles long is the Cedar Hill bike path?

3. Charlie studied for his spelling test for **20** minutes. He studied for his science test for **3** times the amount of minutes than he did for his spelling test. How many minutes did Charlie study for his science test?

4. The cookie recipe calls for **2** cups of butter. The cake recipe calls for $\frac{1}{2}$ a cup of butter. The cookie recipe takes how many times more butter than the cake recipe?

5. Josh scored **3** soccer goals this season. John scored **4** times as many goals as Josh. How many goals did John score?

6. Mike and his grandmother share a birthday. On their next birthday, Mike will be **10** years old. His grandmother will be **7** times his age. How old will Mike's grandmother turn on her next birthday?

13

Read the following passage.

The World's Ocean

The world's oceans cover 70% of the Earth. The oceans are actually one connected body of water. Water from one ocean flows into another. Together, these oceans contain over 95% of the world's water supply.

People divide the world's ocean into five smaller oceans: Pacific, Atlantic, Arctic, Indian, and Antarctic. The Pacific Ocean is the largest. It is located to the west of North and South America. The deepest part of the world's ocean, called the Mariana Trench, is located in the Pacific. The second biggest ocean is the Atlantic. The Atlantic Ocean is located to the east of North and South America. This ocean contains a large underwater mountain range. The Arctic, which is located around the North Pole, is the smallest ocean.

Millions of different plants and animals live in the ocean. The world's largest animal, the blue whale, lives in the ocean. Blue whales are 80 feet long and can weigh over 100,000 pounds! Tiny single-cell plants and animals live in the ocean, too. These single-cell organisms are so small that they cannot be seen without a microscope. Just one cup of ocean water has millions of these tiny plants and animals.

Answer questions about the passage below.

1. Make an inference: Why are the oceans so important for the planet? Explain your answer using information from the passage.

....
....
....

2. Describe the blue whale using two details from the passage.

....
....
....

3. What does the word "organism" mean?

....

....

....

4. Find an excerpt from the passage that explains how small single-cell organisms are.

....

....

....

5. On the map below, label three oceans. Include one fact about each ocean.

....

....

....

FITNESS PLANET → Let's get some fitness in! Go to page 167 to try some fitness activities.

FITNESS

15

Motion is the change in an object's location over time. There are four main factors that affect motion: force, friction, inertia and momentum.

Review the chart below for more information about each of these factors.

Factor	Definition
force	Push or pull
friction	Contact that goes against the motion of an object
inertia	The tendency of an object to stay at rest or preserve its motion
momentum	The force that allows something to continue to move or to grow stronger or faster as time goes on

Directions: On the lines below, write an example of each factor listed above.

1. Force:

....

....

....

2. Friction:

....

....

....

3. Inertia:

....

....

....

4. Momentum:

....

....

....

1. Kylo and Jason visited a pond to skip stones. Kylo skipped 12 stones in the pond, while Jason skipped 10 more stones than Jason. What equation can you use to know how many stones Jason skipped?

2. The pet store sold 9 goldfish over the weekend. It sold 5 more beta fish than goldfish. Write an equation to show how many beta fish were sold.

3. The children set up a lemonade stand and sold 20 cups of lemonade. They sold 3 times as many cookies. Write an equation to show how many cookies were sold.

4. Chris has 30 comic books. This is 4 times as many as Kenny has. Write an equation to show how many comic books Kenny has.

5. Kennison has 3 times as many squishy toys than Cerise. They have a total of 12 squishy toys. Write an equation to show how many squishy toys Kennison has.

6. Colton divided his 35 Pokémon cards between 5 boxes. Write an equation to show how many cards is in each box if they are evenly distributed.

1. An extra-large pizza has 10 slices. If 7 people each take a slice, how many slices will be left after each person has a piece?

....

....

2. A car dealership transports 11 cars by truck. Each truck can hold 2 cars. How many cars will the last truck take?

....

3. Kaydon has 45 tickets at an arcade. Each game costs 4 tickets. After using his tickets to play as many games as he can, how many tickets will Kaydon have leftover?

....

....

4. Mr. Kern has 60 stickers. He gives each of his 22 students the same number of stickers. After giving away as many stickers as he can, how many stickers will Mr. Kern have leftover?

....

....

5. 5 sisters have $16 to spend on candy. Each candy bar costs $3. If each sister buys an equal number of candy bars, how much money will be left?

....

....

FITNESS PLANET → Let's get some fitness in! Go to page 167 to try some fitness activities.

FITNESS

The Topic Sentence

The topic sentence is the sentence that states the main idea of a paragraph.

All of the other sentences in the paragraph support the topic sentence. The topic sentence is often the first sentence in the paragraph, such as in the example below:

Example: **I really like to bake with my family.** Every Sunday morning, my dad and I bake cinnamon rolls while my sister and mom sleep in. We use my grandmother's recipe, and we cover them with delicious icing! My mom and I like to make cookies. Chocolate chip and peanut butter cookies are our favorite. We also make sugar cookies together and decorate them with colorful sprinkles.

Look at the paragraphs below. Each paragraph is missing its topic sentence. Fill in the blank with a topic sentence that you think best fits the paragraph.

1. _____ . First, I love to build snowmen and snow forts. My little sister and I do this together in our backyard. My older brother and I also love to sled down our town's best snow hill. We like to have snowball fights with the neighbors. Finally, I go on winter hikes with my parents. We look at all of the animal footprints in the snow.

2. _____ . First, take out all of the necessary ingredients. Then, mix the dry ingredients together in one bowl and the wet ingredients together in another bowl. Stir the dry ingredients into the wet ingredients just until they are combined. Don't worry if there are a few lumps! Overmixing pancakes makes them tough instead of light and fluffy. Finally, pour the batter onto a preheated griddle. Serve the pancakes with maple syrup!

Read the poem below.

Transformation

A butterfly flits through the warm summer air,
Delicate and light as a tiny feather.

The butterfly stops on a purple blossom,
Drinking in delicious nectar with its long tongue.

It is hard to imagine that just a few months ago
This delicate insect was a wingless, green caterpillar.

But now, this creature is a blaze orange beauty,
Adding one more burst of color to the summer sky.

Answer the following questions about the poem.

1. What is the main idea of the poem?

....
....
....

2. A simile is a comparison of two things using "like" or "as." Find one simile in the poem.

....
....
....

3. The author uses color to create an image in the reader's mind. Find three excerpts from the poem containing color images.

....
....
....

1. Jeremy divides 196 trading cards into pages that hold 8 cards each. How many cards will the partially filled page hold?

....

....

2. Lisa makes 134 party bags. If she puts 5 crayons in each bag for as many bags as she can, how many crayons will the last bag have in it?

....

....

3. Jacque had 145 tulips to plant. She planted them in rows of 10. If she plants as many rows of 10 as she can, how many tulips will Jacque have left?

....

....

4. Chloe puts 156 books on bookshelves. Each shelf can hold 9 books. If Chloe fills each shelf with 9 books, how many books will be on the partially filled shelf?

....

....

5. The library has 742 magazines. Each bin holds 9 magazines. How many magazines will be in the partially filled bin?

....

....

6. Janie made 155 cookies to share with her friends. She puts 4 cookies in each bag. How many cookies will Janie have leftover?

....

At the beginning of European exploration in the late fifteenth and sixteenth centuries, there were a variety of Native American groups inhabiting different regions of the United States. Today, you will compare and contrast several aspects of two of these groups.

Directions: Conduct research on the Native American groups that settled throughout the United States during the 15-16th century. Choose two groups to research and fill out the chart below. You may use books or the internet.

	Group #1:	Group #2:
Style of Housing		
Where They Settled		
Sources of Food & Clothing		
Customs or Traditions		
Political Organization		
Types & Uses of Technology		

FITNESS PLANET → Let's get some fitness in! Go to page 167 to try some fitness activities.

Grade 4-5
WEEK 2

Get ready to explore:

* multi-step word problems
* conjunctions
* speed and energy
* prime/composite numbers and more!

BRAIN HUNTER

1. James sells model planes at craft shows. He charges $24.85 for a large plane. He charges $13.85 for a small plane. Last month he sold 6 large planes and 2 small planes. How much did he make in all?

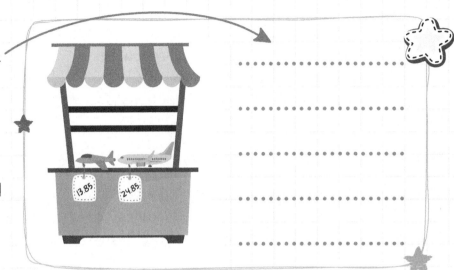

....

....

....

....

....

2. Sarah makes quilts. She uses 24 yards of fabric to make 6 quilts. How many yards of material would she need to make 10 quilts?

....

....

3. The orange team is playing basketball against the green team. Each basket is worth 2 points. The orange team makes 9 baskets. The green team makes 11 baskets. How many more points does the green team have than the orange team?

....

....

4. On Friday, the burger shop sold 291 burgers. On Saturday they sold 210. How many more burgers were sold on Friday than on Saturday?

....

....

5. Jack wants to buy a Christmas gift for his mom that costs $17.99, and one for his dad that costs $14.50. Jack has saved $22.00 so far. How much more money does he need to purchase gifts for his parents?

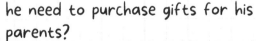

....

....

....

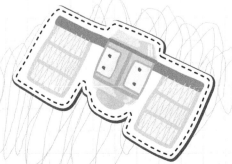

1. Jennie has **3** children. She bought them a pack of **40** pencils and told them to share them equally.

Complete the sentence.
Each child gets [   ] pencils, with [   ] left over.

2. Karlea has been saving **$3** per week for **10** weeks. She wants to buy LOL dolls, which cost **$4** each.

Complete the sentence.
Karlea can buy [   ] dolls, with $ [   ] left over.

3. Jaime made **15** pounds of dough this morning, and **7** pounds this evening. Then, she split it into **4**-pound batches for baking.

Complete the sentence.
Jamie can make [   ] 4-pound batches, with [   ] pounds left over.

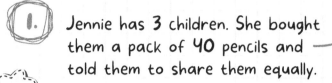

4. Tara is making coloring kits for kids in the hospital. Each kit has **4** crayons and a coloring book. The crayons come in boxes of **10**, and Tara has **3** boxes.

Complete the sentence.
Tara can make [   ] coloring kits, and she will have [   ] crayons left over.

5. Tina is collecting socks at school for the homeless. There are **23** people in her class and each person brought in **3** pairs of socks. They got **32** more pairs from a business donation. Tina thinks they have enough to give about **100** people socks. Does that sound about right?

A. Yes
B. No, that is much too high.
C. No, that is much too low.

A **conjunction** is a word that connects words or groups of words. Some common conjunctions include: *and, but, so* and *or.* Each conjunction has its own meaning and can change the meaning of the sentence.

Examples:

Mike or Charlie rang the doorbell.

Mike and Charlie rang the doorbell.

Circle the conjunctions in the following sentences.

1. I wanted to go outside after school, but my mom said I had to do my homework.
2. I forgot my homework, so I had to walk back to school.
3. Hopefully, a teacher or a custodian is there to let me into the school.
4. I have math and reading homework to complete tonight.

Use conjunctions to combine the following sentences into one. Eliminate any unnecessary words.

1. I ate a snack after school. I did my homework after school.

....

....

2. Ellie did her homework on time. Maggie did not do her homework on time.

....

....

3. I finished my homework quickly. I have time to go outside.

....

....

4. I might go on the swing set. I might go for a bike ride.

....

....

 FITNESS PLANET → Let's get some fitness in! Go to page 167 to try some fitness activities.  FITNESS

Supporting Details

A paragraph should have a topic sentence and several details to support the topic sentence. Using words like "*first*," "*second*," "*next*," and "*finally*" helps to keep these ideas organized. These words are called **transitions**.

Example: Dogs are the best pets. First, dogs can keep you happy! Dogs are always excited to see you, no matter how bad your day was. Next, dogs help you get exercise since dogs need to go on walks every day. Finally, dogs are fun to play with. Dogs can learn tricks and love to play games like catch.

This paragraph has three ideas supporting the main idea that dogs are great pets. The ideas are organized with transition words.

Now read the following paragraph and answer the questions below.

I think cats are better pets than dogs. First, cats are less work. They don't need to go for a walk every day. I live way up north in Upper Michigan, and many days are too cold to go outside for a walk. Also, cats don't jump on guests. Dogs get overexcited and jump on guests, while cats keep their cool. Finally, cats are trained in a litter box. They can be left alone for longer periods of time since they do not need to be let outside.

1. What is the topic sentence of this paragraph?

....

....

2. How many supporting details does this paragraph have?

....

3. Give an example of a supporting detail that is specific from this paragraph.

....

....

4. Find three transition words that the author used to help keep ideas organized.

....

....

Week 2 : Science

Topic 1 : Speed and Energy

Energy is how objects change and move.

Today you will investigate the relationship between the speed of an object and the energy of that object by conducting a simple experiment.

Materials Needed

* Dropper popper (small toy that looks like half of a rubber ball)

Procedure

1. Experiment with the dropper popper to see how you can get it to bounce higher.

2. Record your observations in the space below.

3. Answer the follow up questions.

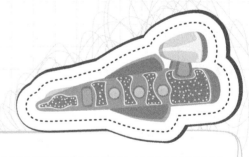

Observations

....
....
....
....
....
....
....

29

Follow-Up Questions

1. What were the results of your experiment?

....
....
....
....

2. Where does the energy for the bounce come from?

....
....
....
....

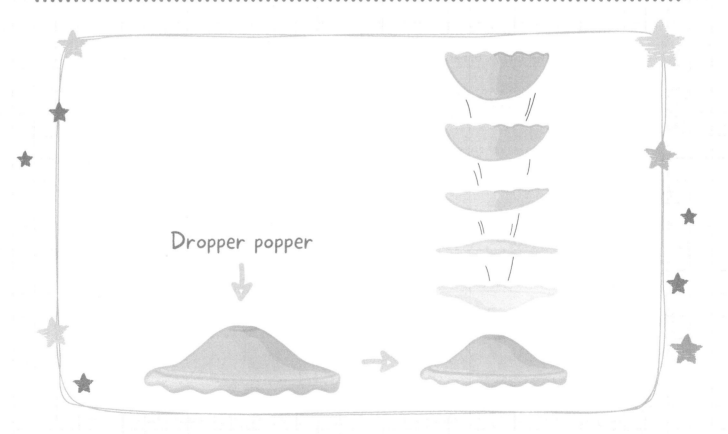

Dropper popper

FITNESS PLANET → Let's get some fitness in! Go to page 167 to try some fitness activities.

FITNESS

1. Juan had 10 peanuts. He ate 4 of them. The letter *p* stands for the number of peanuts Juan has left. Which equation can you use to find *p*?

A. $10 - 4 = p$

B. $\dfrac{10}{4} = p$

2. Keisha bought 12 postcards to send to family and friends. She mails some of them and has 6 left. The letter *p* stands for the number of postcards Keisha mailed. Which equation can you use to find *p*?

A. $12 - p = 6$

B. $\dfrac{12}{p} = 12$

3. A candy company needs to ship 100 pieces of candy to a school. Each box can hold 10 pieces of candy. The letter *c* stands for the number of pieces in each box. Which equation can you use to find *c*?

A. $100 - 10 = c$

B. $\dfrac{100}{10} = c$

4. Three brothers receive 24 action figures for Christmas. They split them evenly between themselves. The letter *a* stands for the number of action figures each child keeps. Which equation can you use to find *a*?

A. $24 - 3 = a$

B. $\dfrac{24}{3} = a$

5. Allison made 12 cupcakes. Her family ate 5. The letter *c* stands for the number of cupcakes that Allison has leftover. Which equation can you use to find *c*?

A. $12 - 5 = c$

B. $\dfrac{12}{5} = c$

6. The classroom has 50 toys and 5 toy bins. The children put an equal number of toys in each bin. The letter *t* stands for the number of toys in each bin. Which equation can you use to find *t*?

A. $50 - 5 = t$

B. $\dfrac{50}{5} = t$

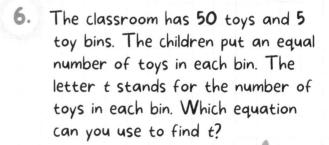

Write prime or composite after each number.

1. **19**

2. **15**

3. **13**

4. **7**

5. **18**

6. **12**

Read the passage below.

Walking on the Moon

On July 16, 1969, the Apollo 11 spacecraft took off with a very special mission: Its astronauts would be the first people to walk on the moon. Other spacecraft had made it to space and back, but no one had yet landed on the moon. The Apollo 11 did just that.

Neil Armstrong and Buzz Aldrin landed on the moon four days after takeoff (a third astronaut stayed in the spacecraft). The astronauts took pictures, collected rocks, and conducted science experiments. They spent a full day on the moon. The landing was shown on live television, and millions of people watched. The three men flew back to Earth in the spacecraft, landing in the Pacific Ocean. They arrived safely on July 24, and many parades were held in their honor.

Answer the following questions about the passage.

1. What is the Apollo 11?

....
....
....
....

2. Create a timeline with three detailed events from July, 1969.

....
....
....
....

3. Why were parades held in honor of the astronauts?

....
....
....
....

4. When Neil Armstrong set foot on the moon, he said, "That's one small step for man, one giant leap for mankind." What do you think he meant by this? Explain your answer.

....

....

....

....

....

5. Aldrin and Armstrong's footprints are still present on the moon's surface. Draw a conclusion: Why do you think this is the case? Use the internet to research if help is needed.

....

....

....

....

....

6. Write two sentences that use conjunctions in the paragraphs above.

....

....

....

....

....

Write prime or composite after each number.

1. 42 →

2. 31 →

3. 79 →

4. 88 →

5. 72 →

6. 67 →

FITNESS PLANET → Let's get some fitness in! Go to page 167 to try some fitness activities.

Two of the earliest settlements in the United States were Jamestown and St. Augustine.
Today, you will choose one of these settlements to research more in depth.

Directions: Research one of the early settlements listed above. Complete the chart below. You may use books or the internet.

	Early Settlement:
Origins	
Physical Structure	
Social Structure	

Grade 4-5
WEEK 3

It's time for a new adventure with:

* factors
* fiction
* energy conversions
* commas and more!

 1. Which of the following numbers are a multiple of **3**?

5, 9, 14 ....

....

 2. Which of the following numbers are a multiple of **6**?

8, 36, 19 ....

....

 3. Which of the following numbers are a multiple of **8**?

8, 22, 18 ....

....

 4. Which of the following numbers are a multiple of **4**?

2, 16, 34 ....

....

 5. Which of the following numbers are a multiple of **2**?

3, 9, 18 ....

....

 6. Which of the following numbers are a multiple of **5**?

30, 16, 12 ....

....

1. Which number is a factor of **32**?

4, 18, 22

2, 16, 20

2. Which number is a factor of **34**?

3. Which number is a factor of **18**?

4, 6, 9

2, 8, 9

4. Which number is a factor of **81**?

5. Which number is a factor of **13**?

1, 6, 9

7, 4, 9

6. Which number is a factor of **24**?

FITNESS PLANET → Let's get some fitness in! Go to page 167 to try some fitness activities.

Read the passage below.

Friendship Troubles

Today something happened at lunch that left Katrina feeling very upset. She walked up to her usual lunch table, and her friends told her there wasn't any room for her. She stood there for a moment, surprised as this had never happened before. No one moved to try to make room for Katrina. She went and sat with some students from another class.

After lunch, Katrina wondered if her friends were mad at her. She had a hard time concentrating on the day's math lesson. She decided that she would ask them at recess.

At recess, she nervously walked up to her friends. She asked if they were mad as tears welled up in her eyes. Her friends immediately came and gave her a hug. They apologized for making her feel upset. They didn't mean to — they were planning a surprise for her birthday on Friday. That was why they pretended there wasn't room at the table.

Katrina breathed a huge sigh of relief. She hugged her friends back, and then they all ran together to the swings.

Answer the following questions about the passage.

1. What is the conflict in the story?

....

....

....

....

2. Find two pieces of textual evidence showing that the conflict had a negative effect on Katrina.

....

....

....

....

3. How was the conflict resolved in the story?

....

....

....

....

4. What is a moral or lesson that readers could learn from this passage? Explain your answer.

....

....

....

....

There are **5** main forms of energy.
See the table below for an example of each.

Energy Form	Definition	Example
Mechanical	Energy that moves	Bicycle
Electrical	Flowing electrons from a plug or battery	Computer
Light (Radiant)	Energy that travels in waves and can be seen	Sun
Heat	Heat moving molecules	Fire
Sound	Energy that travels in waves and can be heard	Singing

Energy can be converted from one form to another.
Review the examples below.

Radiant energy from the sun can be transferred into chemical energy
as trees grow and give off carbon dioxide.

Chemical energy from gasoline can be transferred
into mechanical energy as a car drives.

Directions: Think of two examples of energy conversions and write them below.

1. ....
   ....
   ....

2. ....
   ....
   ....

 FITNESS PLANET → Let's get some fitness in! Go to page 167 to try some fitness activities.

 FITNESS

43

Choose **2** numbers from each table to complete the multiplication sentence.

1.

4	5	6	7

.... × .... = 24

2.

2	3	5	8

.... × .... = 16

3.

5	6	8	9

.... × .... = 54

4.

5	7	9	11

.... × .... = 45

5.

7	8	9	10

.... × .... = 63

6.

3	5	7	9

.... × .... = 27

1. Which two numbers are factor pairs for **75**? (Select all)

    A. 5 and 15

    B. 7 and 10

    C. 3 and 25

2. Which two numbers are factor pairs for **94**? (Select all)

    A. 3 and 31

    B. 2 and 47

    C. 6 and 16

3. Which two numbers are factor pairs for **84**? (Select all)

    A. 2 and 42

    B. 3 and 28

    C. 4 and 21

4. Which two numbers are factor pairs for **66**? (Select all)

    A. 6 and 10

    B. 2 and 33

    C. 6 and 11

5. Which two numbers are factor pairs for **38**? (Select all)

    A. 4 and 9

    B. 2 and 19

    C. 3 and 12

6. Which two numbers are factor pairs for **11**? (Select all)

    A. 1 and 11

    B. 2 and 6

    C. 3 and 3

Commas in a Series

A **series** is a list of three or more similar items in a sentence. A series can be made up of words (example 1) or groups of words (example 2). Notice that commas separate each item in the list.

Example 1: I like apples, bananas, and oranges.

Example 2: I read my language arts textbook, typed my report for science, and finished my math.

> Add commas to separate items in a series as needed in the sentences below.
> Be careful! Some sentences will not need commas.

1.   My mom asked me to walk the dog take out the garbage and unload the dishwasher.

2.   Matthew ate chicken mashed potatoes and broccoli for dinner.

3.   Grandma baked cookies and a cake for the party tonight.

4.   Chantal Gary and Jorge will be at the concert.

5.   I am not sure if Jonathan Melissa or Omar is coming, though.

6.   The students visited the primates farm animals small mammals and big cats sections of the zoo on their field trip.

7.   Neither Jennifer or Carlos can come along on the field trip.

8.   I took my dog for a walk watered the flowers and rolled in the garbage bins.

Concluding Statement

A concluding statement comes at the end of a paragraph. It may restate the main idea in different words. It can also leave your reader thinking about the topic or provide a sense of closure for the paragraph. While this sentence is not always necessary, it does make the paragraph feel complete.

Example:

Dogs are the best pets. Dogs can keep you happy! Dogs are always excited to see you, no matter how bad your day was. Next, dogs help you get exercise since dogs need to go on walks every day. Finally, dogs are fun to play with. Dogs can learn tricks and love to play games like catch. **All in all, dogs help keep their owners healthy and happy.**

Look at the paragraphs below. Each paragraph is missing a closing sentence. Fill in the blank with a closing sentence that you think best fits the paragraph.

1. My family and I enjoy spending time outside during winter. First, we love to build snowmen and snow forts. My little sister and I do this together in our backyard. My older brother and I also love to sled down our town's best snow hill. We like to have snowball fights with the neighbors. Finally, I go on winter hikes with my parents. We look at all of the animal footprints in the snow. _____

2. I think cats are better pets than dogs. First, cats are less work. They don't need to go for a walk every day. I live way up north in Upper Michigan, and many days are too cold to go outside for a walk. Also, cats don't jump on guests. Dogs get overexcited and jump on guests, while cats keep their cool. Finally, cats are trained in a litter box. They can be left alone for longer periods of time since they do not need to be let outside. _____

 FITNESS PLANET → Let's get some fitness in! Go to page 167 to try some fitness activities.

FITNESS

47

What shape or picture comes next?

1.  → ....

2.  → ....

3.  → ....

4.  → ....

5.  → ....

6. → ....

48

There were a number of Early American writers and artists who made important contributions to the new nation's cultural landscape. Some examples include: Paul Revere, Phyllis Wheatley and Benjamin Franklin.

Today, you will choose a writer or artist from this time period to research and write a well-developed paragraph about. Be sure to include who they are, what they were famous for, how they contributed to Early America and why these contributions were important. Remember to write in complete sentences and include correct spelling and appropriate capitalization and punctuation.

Famous Person: ....

....

....

....

....

....

....

....

....

....

....

Grade 4-5
WEEK 4

Let's see what you know about:

* number patterns
* opinion writing
* the Moon
* place value and more!

1. The rule is to multiply by **2**.

15, 30, →

2. The rule is to subtract **4**.

44, 40, →

3. The rule is to divide by **10**.

100, 10, →

4. The rule is to add **8**.

8, 16, →

5. The rule is to multiply by **3**.

6, 18, →

6. The rule is to subtract by **11**.

55, 44, →

FITNESS PLANET → Let's get some fitness in! Go to page 167 to try some fitness activities.

1. Jane wrote the number 40. If the rule is subtract 3, what is the fifth number of her pattern?

2. David wrote a row of numbers following this pattern: 12, 19, 26, 33, 40. What should the next number be?

3. What might be the next three figures in the pattern below?

4. Cynthia wrote the number 6. If the rule is multiply by 3, what is the third number of her pattern.

5. Lori wrote a row of numbers following this pattern: 80, 40, 20, 10. What should the next number be?

6. Alex is writing a row of numbers that follow a pattern. If she uses the rule multiply by five and starts with the number 5, what will the next three numbers be?

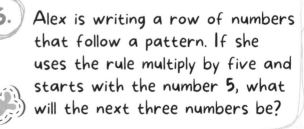

Commas after Introductory Elements

❋ Use commas after introductory words like "first," "however," "next," "meanwhile," "finally," and so forth.

Example: However, you need to complete your homework before you can play.

❋ Use a comma after an introductory clause. Such clauses will start with words such as "after," "while," "since," "when," "although," "because," and so forth.

Example: When I came home from school, there was a surprise waiting for me.

Add a comma to the sentences below using introductory words and clauses.

1. When Sandra comes over you can open that box of cookies.

2. Meanwhile I will be walking home after school.

3. After you walk the dog you can go over to Brian's house.

4. Furthermore the principal will be contacting your parents this evening.

5. Because you were late for school you need to stay after for ten minutes.

6. Since I already saw that movie I decided to stay home.

7. First you need to build the base.

8. Before you jump to conclusions please listen to my explanation.

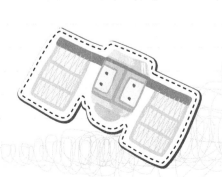

Week 4 Writing

Topic 2 Writing an Opinion Paragraph

Step 1: Prewriting

Consider the following questions. Which one do you have an opinion about? Select one option.

* What is the best place in the world to live?
* What is the most important school subject to study?
* Should students attend school year round?

Next, think about three reasons why you feel this way.

Step 2: Map your Ideas

Now, fill out the graphic organizer below about your opinion.

Topic Sentence:	....
Reason one:	....
	....
	....
Reason two:	....
	....
	....
Reason three:	....
	....
	....

Step 3: Write your Paragraph

Develop these ideas into a full paragraph on a separate sheet of paper. Your paragraph should include:

* a topic sentence
* your three detailed reasons supporting your topic
* a closing sentence
* at least three transitions

The **moon** is a natural object that rotates around the Earth.
It is the second brightest thing in the sky, after the sun.
Just like the sun, the moon rises and sets at different times each day.

Directions: For one week, research the rising and setting times of the moon each night and complete the table below.

Day	Rising Time	Setting Time
1		
2		
3		
4		

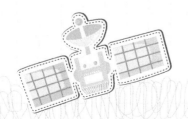

FITNESS PLANET → Let's get some fitness in! Go to page 167 to try some fitness activities.

5		
6		
7		

1. Which number's underlined value is worth **80,000**?

A. 4<u>8</u>3, 667
B. <u>8</u>34, 143
C. 76<u>8</u>, 300

....

....

....

4. Which number's underlined value is worth **300**?

....

....

A. 25<u>3</u>, 611
B. 438, 1<u>3</u>2
C. 154, <u>3</u>22

....

2. What is the value of the underlined digit?

2<u>4</u>0, 439

....

....

5. What is the value of the underlined digit?

239, 4<u>3</u>3

....

....

3. What is the value of the numeral 8 in the number <u>8</u>24, 355?

....

....

6. What is the value of the numeral 6 in the number <u>6</u>24,766

....

....

1. 2,000 is 10 times as much as [____] .

....

....

2. 600 is 10 times as much as [____] .

....

....

3. [____] is 10 times as much as 70.

....

....

4. [____] is 10 times as much as 30.

....

....

5. 300 is $\frac{1}{10}$ of [____] .

....

....

6. 60,000 is 10 times as much as [____] .

....

....

58

Using a Dictionary

Use the following page from a dictionary to answer the questions below.

paper	party
papaya /pə'pīə/ n. a tropical fruit with orange flesh and black seeds	**pardon** /'pärdn/ n. the act of being forgiven for something **pardon** v. to forgive or excuse
paper /pāpər/ n. 1. a material manufactured in thin sheets from wood pulp 2. a newspaper 3. important documents (usually plural) 4. an essay on a topic	**parent** /'pe(ə)rənt/ n. 1. a father or a mother 2. a plant from which a younger one is derived **parent** v. to act as the father or mother of someone
parade /pə'rād/ n. a public procession celebrating an event **parade** v. to walk or march in public	**park** /pärk/ n. 1. a large public garden used for recreation 2. a large enclosed area of nature left untouched for wild animals or recreational use 3. the position of a car in which it doesn't move **park** v. 1. to stop a vehicle and leave it temporarily 2. (informal) to sit down
paragraph /'parə,graf/ n. a section of a piece of writing that deals with a single topic	**parrot** /'parət/ n. a brightly colored bird of the *psittaciformes* order
parallel /'parə,lel/ adj. (for lines, surface, objects) side by side but spaced a continuous equal distance apart **parallel** n. 1. a person or thing that is similar to another 2. the lines of latitude on the earth's surface **parallel** v. 1. to be side by side with something or someone 2. to be similar to something or someone	**party** /'pärtē/ n. 1. a social gathering 2. a political group **party** v. 1. to enjoy oneself at a gathering
129	

1. **Guide words** show the first and last words on the page. What are the guide words for this page of the dictionary, and why are they useful?

. . . .

. . . .

. . . .

FITNESS PLANET → Let's get some fitness in! Go to page 167 to try some fitness activities.

FITNESS

2. Each word has a **part of speech** abbreviation next to it. The part of speech is the category to which a word belongs: noun (n.), verb (v.), adjective (adj.), and so on. What part of speech is the word "*parrot*"?

....
....
....

3. The word "parallel" can be used as more than one part of speech. List the different possible parts of speech for this word.

....
....
....

4. List four possible verbs found on this page of the dictionary.

....
....
....

5. How many definitions are listed for the word "*park*"?

....
....
....

6. Which definition of the word *paper* is used in the sentence below:
I finished writing my paper about natural disasters. ....
....
....

7. Informal or slang definitions are often included in the dictionary. However, the dictionary will always indicate that this is not formal English. What informal definition is included in this page? Write the word and definition below.

....
....
....

1. Write the number.

8 ten thousands, 1 thousand, 8 hundreds, 5 tens, 1 one

....

....

2. Write the number.

6 ten thousands, 2 thousand, 5 hundreds, 6 tens, 3 ones

....

....

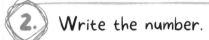

3. In what place is the digit 4?

37, 421

....

....

4. In what place is the digit 2?

12,654

....

....

5. In 924, 326, what digit is in the hundred-thousands place?

....

....

6. In 325,366, what digit is in the thousands place?

....

....

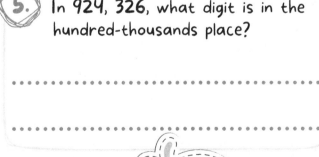

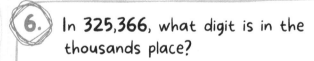
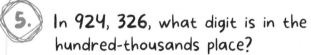
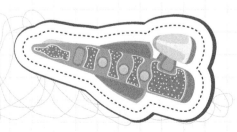

Below is the complete text of the Preamble to the United States Constitution. Read it and answer the questions that follow.

We the People of the United States, in Order to form a more perfect Union, establish Justice, insure domestic Tranquility, provide for the common defence, promote the general Welfare, and secure the Blessings of Liberty to ourselves and our Posterity, do ordain and establish this Constitution for the United States of America.

Directions: Answer the questions that follow.

1. According to the Preamble, what are the six purposes of government?

   A. _____
   B. _____
   C. _____
   D. _____
   E. _____
   F. _____

2. Choose one of these purposes to summarize more in-depth.

   ....
   ....
   ....

3. The 3 main principles on which our government is based are inherent rights, self-government and separation of powers. Choose one of these to summarize more in-depth.

   ....
   ....
   ....

Grade 4-5
WEEK 5

It's time to try your best at:

* converting words to digits
* informational writing
* geological processes
* key ideas about government and more!

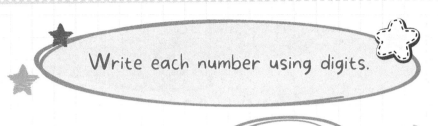

Write each number using digits.

1. five hundred eighty-four →

2. fifty-five →

3. sixty-three →

4. three hundred four →

5. six hundred sixty-two →

6. nine hundred sixty →

64

Write each number using words.

1. 52 → ....

2. 623 → ....

3. 409 → ....

4. 970 → ....

5. 24 → ....

6. 610 → ....

FITNESS PLANET → Let's get some fitness in! Go to page 167 to try some fitness activities.

★ Read the passage from a mystery book below.

The Strange Letter

It was unusually windy and dark that Friday afternoon. I let myself into the house like I did every day after school. It was always an hour before my dad got home from work.

I walked to the kitchen to grab a snack. Then, I headed into the living room to start my reading. It was then that I noticed the letter.

There was a letter, written on bright red paper, stuck in the mail slot on our door. I grabbed the letter and a picture tumbled out. It was a picture of me with my dog Nellie from when I was little. Nellie ran away two years ago.

The letter consisted of nine typed words. It was not signed. All it said was:

MEET ME AT THE PET STORE AT NOON TOMORROW.

Answer the following questions about the passage.

1. **Genre** is a category of books or stories. What elements in the passage indicate that this excerpt is from the mystery genre? List at least two elements.

....
....
....

2. Make a prediction: What do you think happens next? Write a 4-5 sentence summary of your predictions about this mystery.

....
....
....

Step 1: Prewriting

You will be writing a paragraph informing your readers about a certain topic. Which topic do you know a lot about? Select one topic from the following list:

* A type of pet
* A place you have visited
* A holiday that you celebrate

* A sport or hobby that you enjoy
* Anything else!

An informational paragraph does not include your opinion; it only contains facts about the topic. Try to think of three specific facts about your topic of choice. Feel free to do some research if needed.

Step 2: Map your Ideas

Now, fill out the graphic organizer below about your topic.

Topic Sentence:
Specific fact:
Specific fact:
Specific fact:

Step 3: Write your Paragraph

Develop these ideas into a full paragraph on a separate sheet of paper. Your paragraph should include:

* a topic sentence
* your three detailed facts about your topic

* a closing sentence
* at least three transitions
* no opinions

67

Geological processes are the forces that shape the physical makeup of the planet.

Examples of geological processes include:

1. Wind
2. Hurricanes
3. Volcanoes
4. Flooding
5. Avalanches

Geological processes can change the shape of the land suddenly or over time. Today, you are going to explore this more in depth. Research the geological process of your choice and answer the questions below. You may use books or the internet.

1. **Geological Process:**

....
....
....

2. **In what region(s) of the United States does this geological process most commonly occur?**

....
....
....

3. **Does this geological process change the shape of the land suddenly or over time?**

....
....
....

(4.) **How does this geological process change the shape of the land?**

....

....

....

FITNESS PLANET → Let's get some fitness in! Go to page 167 to try some fitness activities.

FITNESS

69

Write each number using digits.

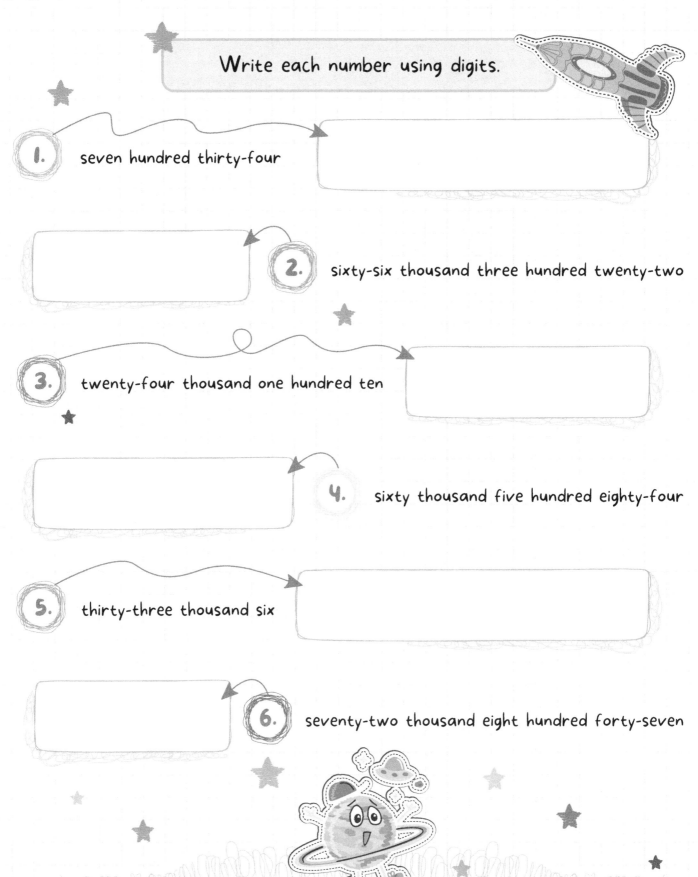

1. seven hundred thirty-four

2. sixty-six thousand three hundred twenty-two

3. twenty-four thousand one hundred ten

4. sixty thousand five hundred eighty-four

5. thirty-three thousand six

6. seventy-two thousand eight hundred forty-seven

Write each number using words.

1. 93,564

2. 42,700

3. 30,567

4. 24,509

5. 14,670

6. 36,678

Parts of an Informational Text: The Table of Contents

Review the following page taken from informational texts.

Table of Contents

1

1. What is this book about? State its topic and a possible title.

....
....
....

2. You want to make tomato soup. What chapter should you turn to?

....
....
....

3. Which chapter is the longest?

....

....

....

4. You need to learn about different types of pots and pans. Where in the book could you learn about this?

....

....

....

5. You want to know which dessert is the healthiest. Where in the book could you learn about this?

....

....

....

6. You want to find a recipe that uses chocolate. What section of the book would help you find a list of possible recipes?

....

....

....

FITNESS PLANET → Let's get some fitness in! Go to page 167 to try some fitness activities.

Write each number using digits.

1. five hundred thirty-four thousand six hundred ninety-eight

....

2. four hundred twenty thousand six hundred seventy-nine

....

3. nine hundred ninety-seven thousand two

....

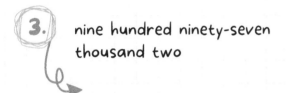

Write each number using words.

4. 253,503

....

....

5. 125, 765

....

....

6. 365,700

....

....

Important documents such as the Declaration of Independence, the Articles of Confederation, the Constitution and the Bill of Rights note several key ideas about government.

Today, you will conduct research in order to define these key ideas.

Directions: Conduct research to better understand the key ideas listed below. Then, match them up with the correct definition.

Key Ideas

1. Union

2. Popular sovereignty

3. Republican government

4. Constitutional government

5. Federalism

6. Individual rights

Definitions

A. Type of government in which power is exercised by representatives chosen by the people

B. Personal, political and economic rights possessed equally by each person

C. An alliance of citizens, colonies, states or other entities for mutual interest or benefit

D. Powers of government are distributed according to the provisions of a constitution or supreme law, which effectively limits or restrains the exercise of power

E. Government by consent of the governed who are the source of all authority in their government

F. Type of government in which power is divided between a federal and national government and the states, such as the United States

Grade 4-5
WEEK 6

Let's see how much you know about:

* comparing numbers
* punctuating titles
* prefixes
* civil responsibility and more!

Use >, <, or = to make each statement true.

$$15{,}478 > 14{,}875$$

1. 48,675 _____ 45,678

2. 22,567 _____ 23,678

3. 2,334 _____ 12,433

4. 34,655 _____ 34,655

5. 8,510 _____ 8,509

6. 2,655 _____ 2,566

FITNESS PLANET → Let's get some fitness in! Go to page 167 to try some fitness activities.

77

Use >, <, or = to make each statement true.

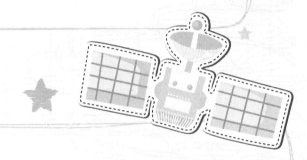

1. 443,566 ◯ 433,665

2. 568,900 ◯ 657,988

3. 243,544 ◯ 234,544

4. 112,322 ◯ 122,321

5. 455,677 ◯ 455,678

6. 214,455 ◯ 214,455

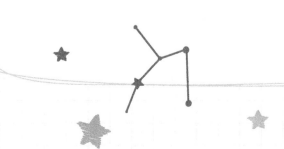

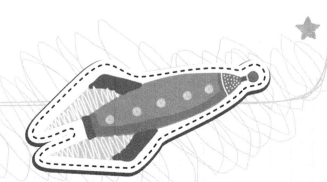

Different types of titles require different punctuation:

* Use quotation marks around titles of **shorter works**. This includes titles of songs, short stories, poems, newspaper/magazine articles, website articles, chapters of books, and episodes of television shows.

* Underline (or *italicize*) titles of **longer works**. This includes titles of movies, albums, books, magazines, newspapers, full websites, and names of television shows.

Examples:
I read the poem "Composed Upon Westminster Bridge" in front of the class.
She read the book <u>Where the Red Fern Grows</u> for a book report.
He watched the episode "The One Where Joey Moves Out" from the television show <u>Friends</u>.

Correctly punctuate the following sentences with titles. Careful! Some sentences have two titles.

1. We read a short story called The Monkey's Paw in language arts class.

   ....

2. Margaret finished reading Out of my Mind for her book report.

   ....

3. The teacher assigned us to read the chapter called Caring for Your Pet over the weekend.

   ....

4. People and Time are two popular magazines.

   ....

5. My favorite poem is Sick from the book Where the Sidewalk Ends.

   ....

6. I read the article American Goldfinch from the website National Geographic Kids.

   ....

Common Prefixes

A prefix is a word part added to the beginning of a base word. A prefix changes the word's meaning, often making the word mean its opposite. Here are some common prefixes and their meanings.

Prefix	Meaning	Example
un-	not	unbelievable
non-	not	nonsense
dis-	opposite of, not	dishonest
pre-	before	preview
re-	again	rewrite
mis-	wrong	misunderstood

Underline the prefixes in the following sentences.

1. I like to read nonfiction books.
2. She had to retype her essay.
3. Callie misbehaved in language arts class.
4. The two wires became disconnected.
5. We took a pretest in math yesterday.

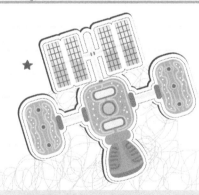

Add the correct prefixes below.

1. not tied → _____ tied
2. heat before → _____ heat
3. play again → _____ play
4. not agree → _____ agree
5. not toxic → _____ toxic

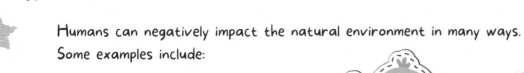

Humans can negatively impact the natural environment in many ways. Some examples include:

1. Pollution of land, water and air
2. Genetic modification of crops
3. Global warming
4. Deforestation

Today, you are going to choose one of the examples above and develop a solution to help reduce the impact on the environment. Think about small things that people, businesses, governments, etc. could do so that the impact is not AS big.

Directions: Answer the questions below.

1. Topic: ....
....

2. When it comes to your topic, how do humans negatively impact the environment?
....
....
....
....
....

FITNESS PLANET → Let's get some fitness in! Go to page 167 to try some fitness activities.

3. If this continues to be a problem, what could happen?

....

....

....

....

....

4. What are possible solutions to reduce the impact of humans on the environment?

....

....

....

....

....

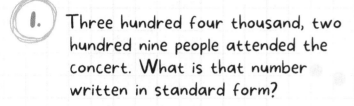

1. Three hundred four thousand, two hundred nine people attended the concert. What is that number written in standard form?

2. What number has **6** ten thousands, **1** thousand, **4** hundreds, the same number of tens as hundreds, and **5** ones?

3. What number has **6** ten thousands, no thousands, **3** hundreds, **3** tens, and **2** ones?

4. Four hundred fifty thousand, six hundred twenty-four people are at the airport. What is that number written in standard form?

5. What number has **3** ten thousands, **3** thousands, no hundreds, **2** tens, and **9** ones?

6. Six hundred seventy-two thousand, nine hundred people visited Kennedy Space Center this year. What is that number written in standard form?

567 → 600

1. Round **689** to the nearest hundred. →

2. Round **254** to the nearest ten. ←

3. Round **24,576** to the nearest thousand. →

4. Round **256,760** to the nearest ten thousand. ←

5. Round **276,900** to the nearest hundred thousand. →

6. Round **975,305** to the nearest thousand. ←

Read the passage below.

Trouble on the Planet Narg

The third moon finally set as the red sun rises above the horizon. I leave my sleeping orb just as my brother leaves his. We greet and go to have our first meal of the day.

Suddenly, there is a bright burning light in the sky. My brother and I leave our family pod to see what it is. Everyone is leaving their pod as well. The light gets closer and closer, and we see that it appears to be a craft or plane of some kind. Everyone starts to nervously talk about what this could be. I run to tell our community's leader.

As I approach the pod of the leader, I see that she is already aware of the bright ship. She is talking to a hologram of planet Narg's leader. I wait patiently on the side. I am surprised that Narg's leader is not worried about this ship.

Answer the following questions about the passage.

1. **Setting** is the time and place of a story. What is the setting of this story?

....
....
....

2. The genre of this book is fantasy. What elements in the passage indicates that this excerpt is from a fantasy book? List at least three elements.

....
....
....

FITNESS PLANET → Let's get some fitness in! Go to page 167 to try some fitness activities.

3.   Even though this story takes place in a fantasy land, what two similarities between Narg and planet Earth?

....
....
....
....

4.   The main character of the passage refers to "sleeping orbs" and "pods." Using context clues, what are these the equivalent of on planet Earth?

   A.   Sleeping orb: _____

   B.   Pod: _____

5.   **Foreshadowing** is when the author gives a hint about what is to come later in the story. Explain how the last line of the passage could be an example of foreshadowing.

....
....
....
....

1. Estimate the sum by rounding each number to the nearest thousand then adding. **34,567 + 23,789**

....

....

2. Estimate the sum by rounding each number to the nearest ten thousand then adding. **24,678 + 57,900**

....

....

3. Estimate the sum by rounding each number to the nearest hundred then adding. **467 + 984**

....

....

4. Estimate the sum by rounding each number to the nearest thousand then adding. **2,794 + 3,235**

....

....

5. Estimate the sum by rounding each number to the nearest ten thousand then adding. **54,618 + 75,325**

....

....

6. Estimate the sum by rounding each number to the nearest ten then adding. **367 + 125**

....

....

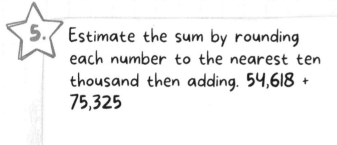

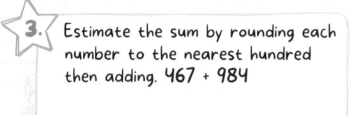

87

Today, you will be identifying and evaluating a contemporary issue that involves civic responsibility, individual rights and the common good. This might be an issue such as payment of property taxes, smoking in public places or proper use of the internet. You should use a variety of resources (books, the internet, interviews of others) to evaluate the issue you choose. Then, write a persuasive argument on whether or not the government should play a role in your particular issue. Be sure to include reasons to support your opinion, as well as correct spelling and appropriate capitalization and punctuation.

The Issue: ....

....

....

....

....

....

....

....

....

....

....

....

....

....

FITNESS PLANET → Let's get some fitness in! Go to page 167 to try some fitness activities.

FITNESS

Grade 4-5
WEEK 7

Now let's learn about:

* estimating sums/differences
* inherited traits
* word roots
* figurative language and more!

1. Estimate the difference by rounding each number to the nearest ten then subtracting. 868 - 568

2. Estimate the difference by rounding each number to the nearest hundred then subtracting. 957 - 653

3. Estimate the difference by rounding each number to the nearest thousand then subtracting. 12,359 - 10,023

4. Estimate the difference by rounding each number to the nearest ten thousand then subtracting. 132,492 - 43,785

5. Estimate the difference by rounding each number to the nearest hundred then subtracting. 1,209 - 468

6. Estimate the difference by rounding each number to the nearest thousand then subtracting. 13,458 - 835

FITNESS PLANET   ➡ Let's get some fitness in! Go to page 167 to try some fitness activities.

FITNESS

1. The Kansas City Chiefs sold 12,476 tickets in section A and 18,365 in section B. Estimate the total number of tickets sold by rounding to the nearest ten thousand.

2. The pencil factory produced **589** yellow pencils and **724** green pencils in one hour. Estimate the total number of pencils produced per hour by rounding to the nearest ten.

3. Sega video games sold **90,453** copies of their newest video game this Christmas season. They sold **54,802** of old video games during the same period. Estimate the total number of video games sold by rounding to the nearest ten thousand.

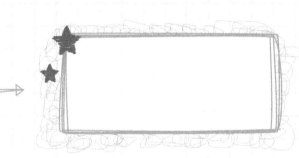

4. A farmer has **124** livestock animals. If **65** are cows, how many are other types of animals? Choose the better estimate: **100** or **60**.

5. A party planner has **1,543** centerpieces. If **963** centerpieces have flowers, how many centerpieces do not have flowers? Choose the better estimate: **600** or **500**.

6. The outlet has **34,028** pieces of clothing. If **23,097** pieces are children's clothing, about how many pieces are adult clothing? Choose the better estimate: **8000** or **11,000**.

Read the following passage.

The Surprise

Mariana woke up early Saturday morning to a quiet house. She walked downstairs to a cold, silent kitchen. Normally, her mom made pancakes for breakfast on Saturdays, and the kitchen was filled with warmth and wonderful aromas.

She went into the living room, and found her mother reading the paper.

"Hola, Mama," Mariana said as she hugged her mother.

"Hola, sweet child," her mother replied with a mischievous smile. Mariana felt like something unusual was happening.

Just then, the back door opened. Mariana's father walked in carrying a small crate. "Are you up already, Mariana?" Papa asked.

Mariana heard a quiet mewing sound coming from the crate. She ran towards it, as she could not wait to see what was inside.

Mariana's father set down the crate and opened the door. Inside there was a tiny gray kitten with blue eyes. Mariana scooped up the kitten immediately.

"Papa, why do you have a cat? Is she ours?" Mariana asked, full of hope. Her mom appeared with a glowing smile on her face.

"Yes, my child," Papa said gently. "She is ours."

Answer the questions about the passage below.

1. Realistic fiction is a genre about stories that are made up but could actually happen in real life today. What elements in the passage indicate that this excerpt is from a piece of realistic fiction? List at least two elements.

....

....

....

....

2. Early in the passage, the author foreshadows that something special or different is going on. Provide an example of foreshadowing from the beginning of the text.

....

....

....

....

3. **Sensory details** are details in a story that appeal to the reader's senses (seeing, feeling, smelling, tasting, and hearing). Provide three examples of sensory details from the text.

....

....

....

....

....

....

4. Using context clues, provide definitions for the following words:

Mischievous: ....

Aromas: ....

5. Give an example of a sentence that uses a comma after an introductory word.

....

....

An **inherited trait** is a characteristic that is passed down from a parent to a child.

Examples of traits include:

Eye color	**Hair color**	**Skin tone**
Height	**Hair type**	**Allergies**

Let's begin exploring inherited traits by thinking about the similarities and differences between you and your parents.

Directions: Answer the questions below.

I. **How are you similar to your parents?**

....

....

....

....

2. How are you different than your parents?

....

....

....

....

....

....

....

3. What traits do you think you inherited from your parents?

....

....

....

....

....

....

....

4. How might inherited traits be similar for plants and animals?

....

....

....

....

....

....

FITNESS PLANET → Let's get some fitness in! Go to page 167 to try some fitness activities.

FITNESS

1. Estimate the product. Round the second factor to the nearest ten, then multiply. **4 x 23**

2. Estimate the product. Round the second factor to the nearest ten, then multiply. **5 x 147**

3. Estimate the product. Round the second factor to the nearest ten, then multiply. **8 x 34**

4. Estimate the product. Round the second factor to the nearest hundred, then multiply. **2 x 254**

5. Estimate the product. Round the second factor to the nearest hundred, then multiply. **6 x 122**

6. Estimate the product. Round the second factor to the nearest hundred, then multiply. **9 x 789**

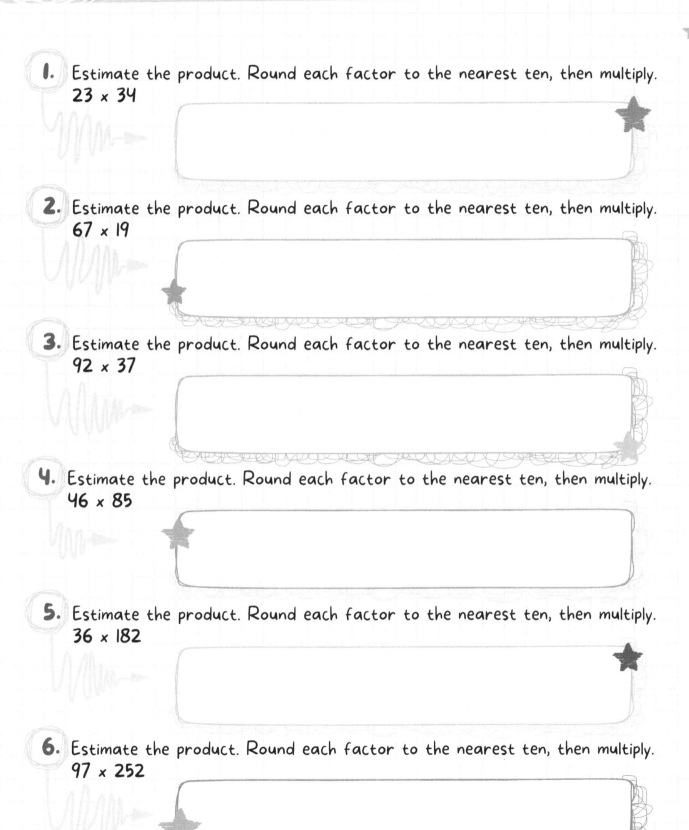

1. Estimate the product. Round each factor to the nearest ten, then multiply.
23 x 34

2. Estimate the product. Round each factor to the nearest ten, then multiply.
67 x 19

3. Estimate the product. Round each factor to the nearest ten, then multiply.
92 x 37

4. Estimate the product. Round each factor to the nearest ten, then multiply.
46 x 85

5. Estimate the product. Round each factor to the nearest ten, then multiply.
36 x 182

6. Estimate the product. Round each factor to the nearest ten, then multiply.
97 x 252

97

Word Roots

A root is the word base upon which a prefix or suffix can be added. Knowing a word root can help you understand other words containing that root. Here are some common roots and their meanings.

Roots	Meaning	Example
meter	measure	thermometer
phobe/phobia	fear	hydrophobia
graph	written	autograph
scrib/script	to write	scribble
spect	to see or watch	inspect
photo	light	photocopy

Underline the roots in the following sentences.

1. The witness described the event.
2. The plant produces food using photosynthesis.
3. My sister suffers from arachnophobia.
4. Photograph means "light writing."
5. We measured the perimeter of the circle.

Add the missing root below. You will use the roots from the table above.

1. instrument that measures atmospheric pressure ➡ baro............
2. written life story ➡ bio............y
3. one who watches ➡ ....ator
4. fear of closed spaces ➡ claustro............
5. written medical instructions ➡ pre............ions

Literal language is when the writer means exactly what they say. **Figurative language** goes beyond the meaning of the exact words used to create a more interesting effect.

> Literal language: **She was so nervous she was shaking.**
>
> Figurative language: **She was so nervous she was shaking like a fish out of water.**

Both of these sentences indicate that the woman was shaking or trembling. The sentence with figurative language does not mean that the woman was a fish. Those words are used figuratively to create a more interesting effect.

Review some examples of figurative language below.

Simile: a comparison between two unlike things using like or as

> Example: **She was as lazy as a sloth.**

Metaphor: a comparison between two unlike things without using like or as

> Example: **She was an elegant swan up on stage.**

Idioms: a figurative expression that is universally used in a language

> Example: **It is raining cats and dogs.**

Use figurative language to describe the following:

1. Something loud: ....

2. Something quiet: ....

3. Something tiny: ....

4. Something huge: ....

5. Something cold: ....

6. Something hot: ....

FITNESS PLANET → Let's get some fitness in! Go to page 167 to try some fitness activities.  FITNESS

99

1. Round the first number to the nearest ten and divide. 525 ÷ 4 =

2. Round the first number to the nearest ten and divide. 78 ÷ 2 =

3. Round the first number to the nearest ten and divide. 492 ÷ 5 =

4. There are **667** dominoes. If each box holds **6** dominoes, about how many boxes will it take to contain all the dominoes? Choose the better estimate. **110** or **200**

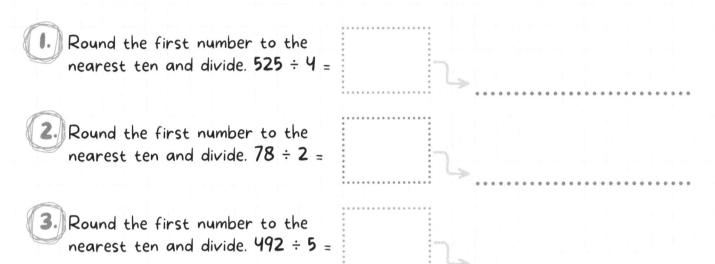

5. There are **298** students going to the state capitol. If **5** students can fit in a car, about how many cars are needed to transport students? Choose the better estimate. **30** or **60**

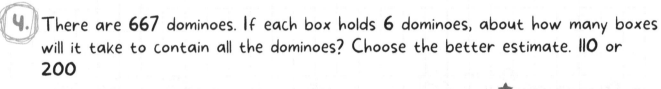

6. There are **275** ornaments on the Christmas tree. If each box holds **12** ornaments, about how many boxes are needed to store the ornaments? Choose the better estimate. **23** or **33**

Today, you will be looking at and analyzing the locations of Native American and Colonial settlements in Early America.

Directions: Find a map online of Native American and Colonial settlements in Early America to study. Then, answer the questions below.

1. What do you notice about where Native Americans and colonists tended to settle? Think about the things that may be near the locations of the settlements.

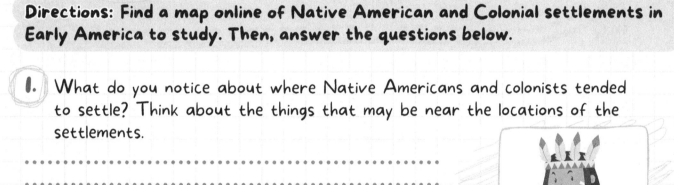

....
....
....
....
....
....

2. Give two examples to support your answer from question #1.

* ....
....
* ....
....

3. Why do you think the Native American groups and colonists decided to settle in these locations?

....
....
....
....
....
....

Grade 4-5
WEEK 8

Get ready for a new adventure with:

* multi-digit numbers
* suffixes
* animal adaptations
* area models and more!

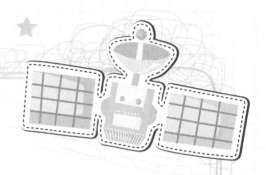

Add.

1.
$$
\begin{array}{r}
397 \\
+\ 287 \\
\hline
\end{array}
$$

2.
$$
\begin{array}{r}
294 \\
+\ 109 \\
\hline
\end{array}
$$

3.
$$
\begin{array}{r}
1,237 \\
+\ 4,598 \\
\hline
\end{array}
$$

4.
$$
\begin{array}{r}
34,972 \\
+\ 28,197 \\
\hline
\end{array}
$$

5.
$$
\begin{array}{r}
35,092 \\
+\ 25,609 \\
\hline
\end{array}
$$

6.
$$
\begin{array}{r}
1,891 \\
+\ 4,328 \\
\hline
\end{array}
$$

Subtract.

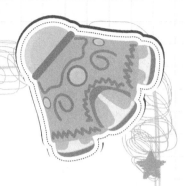

1.
$$31{,}209$$
$$-\ 16{,}242$$

2.
$$428$$
$$-\ 299$$

3.
$$1{,}973$$
$$-\ 1{,}357$$

4.
$$3{,}509$$
$$-\ 2{,}487$$

5.
$$23{,}405$$
$$-\ 14{,}879$$

6.
$$5{,}248$$
$$-\ 3{,}005$$

FITNESS PLANET → Let's get some fitness in! Go to page 167 to try some fitness activities.

FITNESS

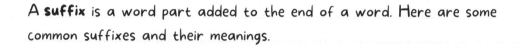

Common Suffixes

A **suffix** is a word part added to the end of a word. Here are some common suffixes and their meanings.

Suffix	Meaning	Example
-er, -or	one who	survivor
-ology	study of	geology
-able, -ible	can do, able	capable
-ful	full of	careful
-ly	in the manner of	friendly

Underline the roots in the following sentences.

1. The train conductor rang the bell.
2. The movie was enjoyable.
3. My mom is very helpful with my homework.
4. I quickly ran to my class.
5. She specializes in neurology.

Add the missing root below. You will use the roots from the table above.

1. in a loving manner ⟹ loving...........................

2. study of life ⟹ bio...........................

3. full of pain ⟹ pain...........................

4. can be seen ⟹ vis...........................

5. one who boxes ⟹ box...........................

105

Read the poem. Then, answer the questions that follow.

The Beach

Sparkling diamond sand covers the shore,
White seagulls screeching from above.

Gentle waves lap at the coast,
As children play in the sapphire water.

The sun shines like a gemstone in the sky,
Happily watching over the children below.

Answer the following questions about the passage.

1. Find a simile in the poem. Explain its figurative meaning.

....
....

2. Find a metaphor in the poem. Explain its figurative meaning.

....
....

3. **Personification** is when an author gives human characteristics to an object. Find an example of personification in the poem.

....
....
....

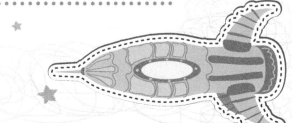

An **adaptation** is a special skill or physical characteristic that helps an animal survive in its environment.

Examples of physical characteristics that are adaptations include: beaks, feet or body coverings.

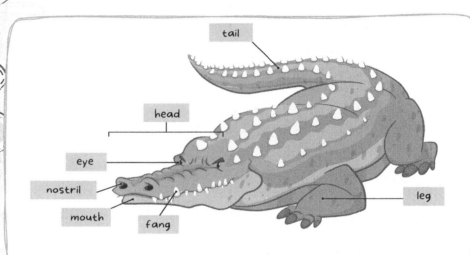

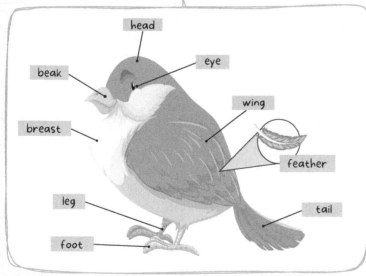

Today, you will draw the animal of your choice, label the physical characteristics that help it to survive in its environment and explain any other adaptations the animal may have.

FITNESS PLANET → Let's get some fitness in! Go to page 167 to try some fitness activities.

FITNESS

Sketch:

What animal did you draw? Which characteristics help this animal to survive?

....
....
....
....
....
....
....

Other adaptations that help the animal survive in its environment (skills, etc.):

....
....
....
....
....
....

Fill in the missing digit.

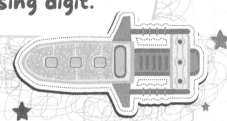

1.

$$
\begin{array}{r}
5,246 \\
+\ 1,3\underline{\ \ }6 \\
\hline
6,602
\end{array}
$$

2.

$$
\begin{array}{r}
2,50\underline{\ \ } \\
+\ 8,109 \\
\hline
10,612
\end{array}
$$

3.

$$
\begin{array}{r}
12,495 \\
+\ 1\underline{\ \ },394 \\
\hline
29,889
\end{array}
$$

4.

$$
\begin{array}{r}
3,791 \\
-\ 2,1\underline{\ \ }8 \\
\hline
1,663
\end{array}
$$

5.

$$
\begin{array}{r}
\underline{\ \ }98 \\
-\ 479 \\
\hline
319
\end{array}
$$

6.

$$
\begin{array}{r}
6,209 \\
-\ 4,\underline{\ \ }64 \\
\hline
2,145
\end{array}
$$

1. $10 \times 6 =$ [ ]

2. $8 \times 7 =$ [ ]

3. $12 \times 4 =$ [ ]

4. $3 \times 11 =$ [ ]

5. $7 \times 6 =$ [ ]

6. $9 \times 7 =$ [ ]

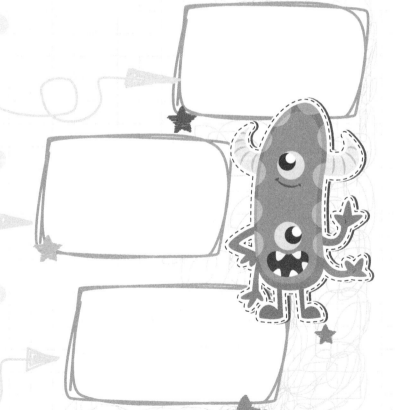

Read the following passage.

Jellyfish

Even though jellyfish do not have a brain, they have been on Earth for longer than dinosaurs. Jellyfish are found in all of the oceans. Despite their name, they are not technically a "fish." Jellyfish do not have a backbone, so they are actually classified as an invertebrate. With no brain, backbone, or eyes, jellyfish do not control much of their movements. Instead, they float wherever the ocean currents take them. This doesn't bother jellyfish as they are very resilient. They can live in cold or warm water. They can also live in deep or shallow water. And, jellyfish can eat almost anything, so they are happy wherever the ocean's currents take them.

Most jellyfish have a body shaped like a bell. There are long, stinging tentacles that come out from the bottom of that bell shape. The mouth is located in the center of that bottom bell shape as well. Their body is soft and made up of **95%** water!

1. **Draw and label a diagram of a jellyfish with three details about their bodies.**

FITNESS
PLANET → Let's get some fitness in! Go to page 167 to try some fitness activities.

FITNESS

111

2. Write two unusual facts about jellyfish.

....

....

3. Using context clues, define the following:

Invertebrate: ....

Resilient: ....

Currents: ....

4. Make an inference: How have jellyfish been able to survive so long?

....

....

....

....

....

....

1. Which model represents 4 x 15?

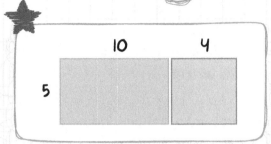

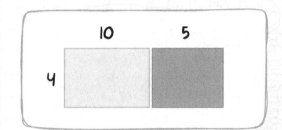

2. Use the model to find 3 x 12.

3 x 12 = ...

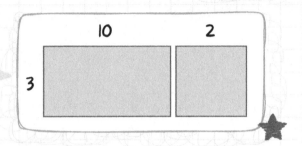

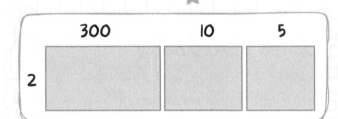

3. Use the model to find 2 x 315.

2 x 315 = ...

4. Which model represents 5 x 411?

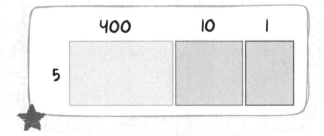

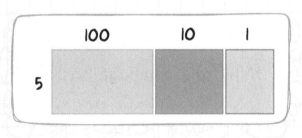

5. Use the area model to find 64 x 38.

64 x 38 = ...

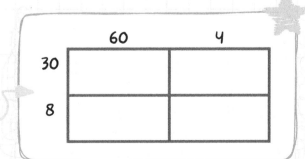

A **drainage basin** is any area of land where precipitation collects and drains off into a common outlet, such as into a bay, river or other body of water.

Drainage basins connect into other drainage basins at lower elevations and drain into a common outlet.

Directions: Locate a map of the drainage basins in the United States online. Then, answer the questions below.

1. List the 12 drainage basins in the United States below.

1. ....
2. ....
3. ....
4. ....
5. ....
6. ....

7. ....
8. ....
9. ....
10. ....
11. ....
12. ....

2. Why are drainage basins important?

....
....
....
....
....
....
....

FITNESS PLANET → Let's get some fitness in! Go to page 167 to try some fitness activities.

Grade 4-5
WEEK 9

It's time to test your skills on:

* properties
* commas and interjections
* informational texts
* ecosystems and more!

1. 20 x 20 = ☐

2. 90 x 80 = ☐

3. 130 x 40 = ☐

4. 50 x 5 = ☐

5. 80 x 9 = ☐

6. 60 x 120 = ☐

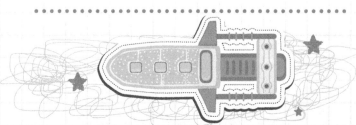

1. Which property of multiplication is shown here? 9 x 5 = 5 x 9

   A. associative

   B. communicative

   C. distributive

   D. zero

2. Which property of multiplication is shown here? 0 x 5 = 0

   A. associative

   B. communicative

   C. distributive

   D. zero

3. Which property of multiplication is shown here?
   8 x 1 + 8 x 0 = 8 x (1 + 0)

   A. associative

   B. communicative

   C. distributive

   D. zero

4. Which equation shows the identity property of multiplication?

   A. 0 x 7 = 0

   B. 1 x 8 = 8

   C. 3 + 36 = 3 + 6 x 6

   D. 5 x 4 = 4 + 4 + 4 + 4 + 4

5. If 70 ÷ 7 = 10,

   then .... x 10 = 70

6. Write a related fact for

   81 ÷ 9 = 9

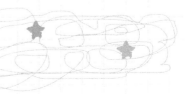

Commas with Interjections.

An **interjection** is a an abrupt remark that is not a necessary part of a sentence. Often, an interjection is said with a lot of emotion. In that case, it is followed by an exclamation point.

Example: Ouch! I just hit my knee.

If it is said with less emotion, it is set off from the rest of the sentence with a comma.

Example: Hey, we should finish our homework.

Common interjections are "**okay**," "**darn**," and "**well**."

Add a comma as needed to set off interjections in the sentences below.

1. Gee I didn't realize that she was feeling left out.

2. Uh-oh I think we forgot to buy dog food.

3. Shhhh the baby is sleeping.

4. Aw that was so kind of you to help out.

5. Well she didn't have to be rude about it.

Read the passage below.

Tsunamis

A tsunami is a type of natural disaster that occurs when huge ocean waves develop suddenly. Tsunamis can develop when an earthquake or volcanic eruption happens under the ocean. These events create enormous waves that travel fast. There is very little warning that a tsunami is about to hit a shore. Tsunamis are very powerful: they can uproot trees, wash cars and houses out to the ocean, and even destroy a whole town.

Now answer the questions below about the passage.

1. Summarize the passage in one to two sentences.

....

....

....

2. Explain how tsunamis form.

....

....

....

3. Find a piece of textual evidence that supports the idea that tsunamis can be very strong.

....

....

....

....

FITNESS PLANET → Let's get some fitness in! Go to page 167 to try some fitness activities.

An **ecosystem** is a community of living organisms and the nonliving parts of their environment.

Today, you will research two different ecosystems and compare and contrast the plants and animals in them.

Examples of ecosystems:

Grasslands

Deserts

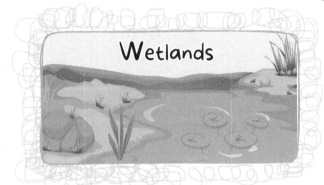

Wetlands

Oceans

Forests

Tundras

Directions: Choose two different ecosystems and research each. Fill out the table below with the information you learn. Then, answer the questions that follow.

	Ecosystem #1	Ecosystem #2
Description of the Ecosystem		
Plants Found in the Ecosystem		
Animals Found in the Ecosystem		

Follow-Up Questions:

1. How are these ecosystems alike?

2. How are these ecosystems different?

1. $56 \div 7 =$ [ ]

....

....

2. $121 \div 11 =$ [ ]

....

3. $2 \overline{)5\ 6\ 4}$

4. $6 \overline{)2\ 4\ 1\ 8}$

5. $31 \div 5 =$ [ ] R [ ]

....

....

6. $365 \div 2 =$ [ ] R [ ]

....

....

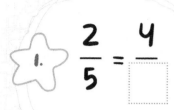

1. $\dfrac{2}{5} = \dfrac{4}{\square}$

5. $\dfrac{2}{30} = \dfrac{1}{\square}$

2. $\dfrac{3}{4} = \dfrac{\square}{12}$

6. $\dfrac{4}{20} = \dfrac{\square}{100}$

3. $\dfrac{5}{10} = \dfrac{\square}{100}$

4. $\dfrac{6}{8} = \dfrac{18}{\square}$

 FITNESS PLANET → Let's get some fitness in! Go to page 167 to try some fitness activities.

 FITNESS

Sentence fluency is when writing has smooth, flowing sentences of varying lengths. Sometimes writing lacks this fluency because it contains too many short sentences. In this case, it is good to combine sentences to create longer, smoother sentences.

Consider the following group of sentences:

Jellyfish can be found in any ocean.
Jellyfish can eat almost anything.
Jellyfish can survive in any type of water.
Jellyfish do not have a brain.
Jellyfish have been around longer than the dinosaurs.

These sentences can be combined in a number of ways.

1. Combine sentences using conjunctions

    Jellyfish do not have a brain but have been around longer than dinosaurs!
    Jellyfish can survive in any type of water, so they can be found in any ocean.

2. Create a series

    Jellyfish can be found in any ocean, can eat almost anything, and can survive in any type of water.

3. Create an introductory clause

    Because jellyfish can eat almost anything, they can be found in any ocean.
    Even though jellyfish do not have a brain, they have been around longer than the dinosaurs.

4. Create one simple sentence using two ideas

The brainless jellyfish can eat anything.

Now practice combining sentences.

1. Create four different sentence combinations using some of the following sentences.

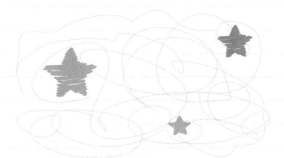

The octopus has eight arms.

The octopus's arms are lined with suckers.

The octopus is an invertebrate.

The octopus can fit in tiny spaces.

The octopus uses camouflage to hide.

....

....

....

....

2. Create four different sentence combinations using some of the following sentences.

The anglerfish lives in the deepest part of the ocean.

Anglerfish produce their own light.

Anglerfish can survive in very cold water.

Anglerfish can eat a fish twice its size.

Anglerfish have a very large mouth.

....

....

....

....

Compare fractions using <, >, or =.

1. $\dfrac{1}{10}$ ◯ $\dfrac{1}{5}$

4. $\dfrac{8}{8}$ ◯ $\dfrac{10}{11}$

2. $\dfrac{15}{16}$ ◯ $\dfrac{9}{11}$

5. $\dfrac{7}{10}$ ◯ $\dfrac{1}{2}$

3. $\dfrac{7}{14}$ ◯ $\dfrac{1}{5}$

6. $\dfrac{8}{16}$ ◯ $\dfrac{13}{14}$

There are **8** physical regions in the United States. **Physical regions** are areas of land divided by natural borders such as a mountain range.

Directions: Locate a map of the 8 physical regions of the United States online. Then, answer the questions below.

1. List and give a brief description of each of the 8 physical regions of the United States.

1. ....

2. ....

3. ....

4. ....

5. ....

6. ....

7. ....

8. ....

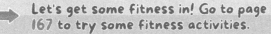

FITNESS PLANET → Let's get some fitness in! Go to page 167 to try some fitness activities.

127

Grade 4-5
WEEK 10

Come along on a journey with:

* fractions
* synonyms/antonyms
* engineering
* decimals and more!

4. $1\frac{3}{4} + 2\frac{3}{8} =$

1. $\frac{2}{10} + \frac{3}{10} =$

5. $2\frac{1}{4} - 1\frac{1}{8} =$

2. $\frac{3}{6} - \frac{2}{6} =$

6. $5 - 3\frac{1}{2} =$

3. $\frac{3}{3} - \frac{2}{3} =$

129

1. $4 \times \dfrac{1}{4} =$ ☐

2. $\dfrac{1}{3} \times 6 =$ ☐

3. $2 \times \dfrac{5}{2} =$ ☐

4. $9 \times \dfrac{1}{3} =$ ☐

5. $\dfrac{1}{5} \times 5 =$ ☐

6. $3 \times \dfrac{2}{3} =$ ☐

Topic 1 Synonyms and Antonyms

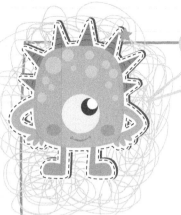

A **synonym** is a word that means the same as another.

An **antonym** is a word that means the opposite of another.

Synonyms and antonyms can help you find more ways to express an idea. They can help you avoid being repetitive by repeating the same word over and over. Both synonyms and antonyms can be found in a thesaurus.

Explain the relationship (synonym or antonym) in the word pairs below. Use a thesaurus or dictionary for help if necessary.

1. happy: content

   These words are ....

2. excited: bored

   These words are ....

3. calm: tranquil

   These words are ....

4. angry: infuriated

   These words are ....

5. drowsy: energetic

   These words are ....

A personal narrative details a short event from your life. The event can be funny, serious, sad, or happy. The goal is to add specific sensory details to make the event easy to picture in the mind of your reader.

Step 1:

Think of one event from your life, and write a short one-sentence summary of the incident below.

Topic: ....
....

Step 2:

Now, describe what happened during the event. Include specific sensory details.

Sense: .... **Details:** ....
....

Sense: .... **Details:** ....
....

Sense: .... **Details:** ....
....

Step 3:

Now, use these thoughts to write a vivid personal narrative paragraph on another sheet of paper. Be sure to write in complete sentences. Your paragraph should include:

* A topic sentence introducing the event
* Sensory details describing the event
* A closing sentence

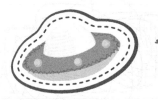

Today, you will explore **engineering** (the design, building and use of machines) by designing a machine that helps fill a need in your life. First, you should identify a need for which you want to build a machine. It may be helpful to think about tasks or chores that could be made easier with the help of a machine. Then, you should sketch your **prototype**, or preliminary model. Last, you will build your prototype using household objects. Use the organizer below to plan your work.

Your Need:

....

....

Sketch of your Prototype:

 FITNESS PLANET → Let's get some fitness in! Go to page 167 to try some fitness activities.

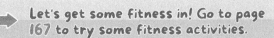

Household Materials Needed to Build Your Machine:

....

....

....

....

....

....

....

....

....

....

....

....

....

....

....

....

....

....

1. Write $\dfrac{3}{10}$ as a decimal:

....

2. Write $\dfrac{9}{100}$ as a decimal:

....

3. Write $\dfrac{5}{10}$ as a decimal:

....

4. Write $\dfrac{68}{100}$ as a decimal:

....

5. Write .4 as a fraction:

....

6. Write .6 as a fraction:

....

1. Michael hung a mirror on the wall. What is the perimeter of the mirror?

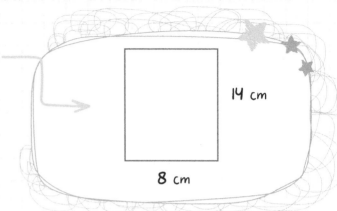

14 cm

8 cm

....

2. The width of the basketball court is 20 feet. The length is twice as long as its width. What is the perimeter of the basketball court?

....

3. A frame has two 5-inch sides and two 7-inch sides. What is the area?

....

4. A board has a length of 10 inches and a width of 4 inches. What is the area?

....

5. A rectangular window has an area of 120 square inches. The height of the widow is 8 inches. What is the width of the window?

....

6. The area of a banner is 32 square feet. If the length of the banner is 4 feet, what is its width?

....

Read the following excerpt from a historic diary.

Going West

My parents immigrated from Ireland before I was born. My father had always been a farmer in Ireland, but here in Boston, he was forced to find other work. He worked long hours at his factory job, often 14 to 16 hours a day. Even still, we could never afford to buy any land in the Boston area.

Since coming from Ireland, my parents had me and my three younger siblings. My mother is expecting another baby in a few months. Our tiny apartment is crowded, and there are many mouths to feed.

My father has always dreamed of owning land and farming again. He and my mother missed the countryside. Boston was crowded, loud, and dirty. A house in the country with land was their dream.

Last year, the government passed an act that allowed people to get 160 acres of land out west. Best of all: The land would be free if we lived on it for five years. My father and mother talked it over for days, and they made their decision. Our family was moving west.

FITNESS PLANET → Let's get some fitness in! Go to page 167 to try some fitness activities.

Now, answer the following questions about the passage.

1. Historical fiction is a genre about stories that are made up but could actually have happened during a period in history. Which elements in the passage indicate that this excerpt is from a piece of historical fiction? List at least two elements.

....

....

....

2. State two reasons why people moved westward, according to this passage.

....

....

....

3. In 1862, the United States government passed the Homestead Act, which the protagonist refers to in this excerpt. Describe what you know about the Homestead Act from this journal.

....

....

....

4. Write a three sentence summary of this family's experience (as depicted in this excerpt).

....

....

....

....

....

....

Is each angle acute, right, or obtuse?

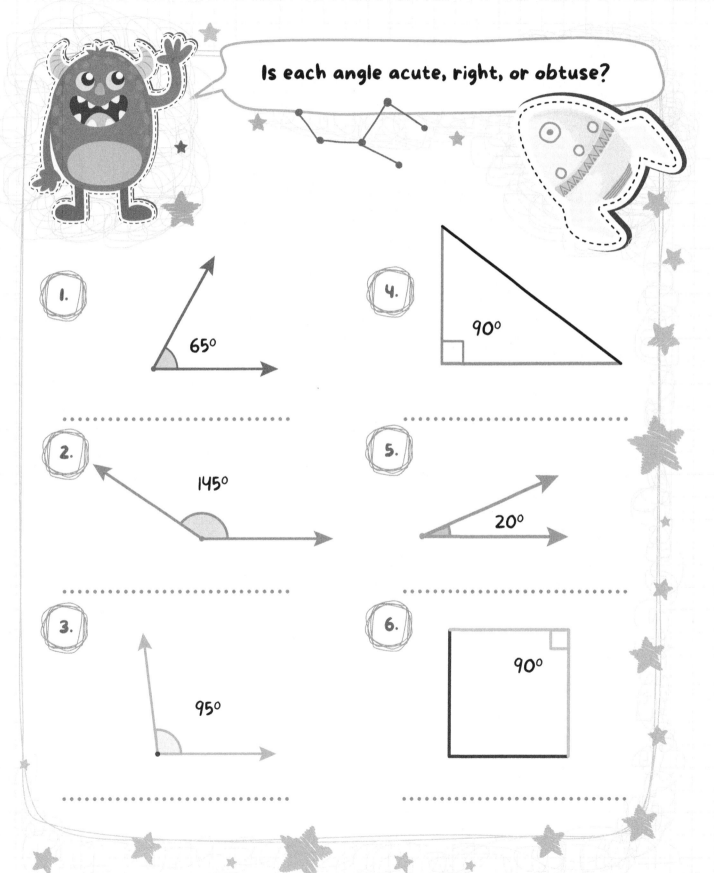

1. 65°

2. 145°

3. 95°

4. 90°

5. 20°

6. 90°

139

Today, you will use a map or globe to identify a variety of major cities, waterways and mountain ranges in the United States. You can either use a map from the Internet or a globe.

Directions: Locate each of the following on a map or globe.

1. Colorado ....

2. Massachusetts ....

3. Oregon ....

4. Alabama ....

5. State Capital of Indiana ....

6. State Capital of Arizona ....

7. Los Angeles ....

8. Chicago ....

9. Mississippi River ....

10. Ohio River ....

11. Lake Michigan ....

12. Lake Huron ....

13. Smoky Mountains ....

14. Rocky Mountains ....

15. Cascade Mountains ....

Grade 4-5
WEEK 11

Now let's get to work on:

* homographs
* commas and tag questions
* engineering
* personal budgeting and more!

1. 16 = 4 × 4

 .... is 4 times as much as 4.

2. Tyler has **35** tickets at the fair. Each activity costs **6** tickets. After using his tickets to play as many games as he can, how many tickets will Kaydon have leftover?

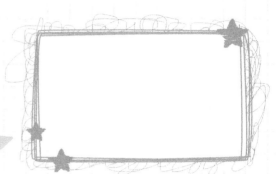

3. Joy has 10 Skittles. She eats **3** of them. The letter s stands for the number of Skittles Joy has left. Which equation can you use to find s?

A. 10 − 3 = s
B. 10 ÷ 3 = s

4. Which number is a factor of **36**? 3, 15, 20

....
....

5. What shape comes next?

1. Estimate the product. Round each factor to the nearest ten, then multiply.

19 × 53

2. Twenty ten thousands, 4 thousands, 2 hundreds, 8 ones

3.

6	7	8	9

.... × .... = 48

4. 58,523 ◯ 58,532

5. Use the model to find 6 × 14.

6 × 14 = ...

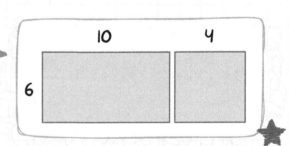

6. Is the angle acute, right, or obtuse?

45°

....

FITNESS PLANET → Let's get some fitness in! Go to page 167 to try some fitness activities.

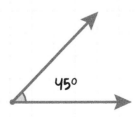

143

A **homograph** is a word that is spelled the same as another but they have different meanings. They are not necessarily pronounced the same.

Example:

I tied a **bow** in my sister's hair.

The hunter uses a **bow** and arrow.

The actress took a **bow** at the end of her performance.

The first sentence uses "bow" to mean a knot tied with two strings. The second sentence uses "bow" to mean a curved piece of wood joined by a string. In the third sentence, "bow" is pronounced differently, even though it is spelled the same. Here "bow" means the act of bending the head or body forward as a sign of respect.

The following words are homographs. Write a sentence for each meaning of the homograph. Use a dictionary if you need help.

1. **duck**

meaning 1: ....

meaning 2: ....

2. **pitcher**

meaning 1: ....

meaning 2: ....

3. **bark**

meaning 1: ....

meaning 2: ....

Commas after Tag Questions and Response Words

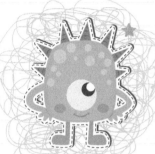

A tag question is a short question added to the end of a sentence. Tag questions are separated from the rest of the sentence by a comma.

Example:

You know the answer, don't you?

Example:

Yes, I do know the answer.

Response words are answers to questions. They are also separated from the rest of the sentence by a comma or commas.

Add a comma as needed to the sentences below.

1. She was late again wasn't she?

2. The dog doesn't bite does it?

3. No my dog is very friendly and never bites anyone.

4. Sure you can come along on the trip.

5. It's going to rain again isn't it.

6. Yes it does look like it is going to rain.

145

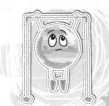

Last week you explored engineering by designing and building a machine to assist with a need from your own life. Today, you will answer questions about your machine and how well it worked.

1. What is the need that your machine helps with?

....
....
....
....

2. How does it help to meet this need?

....
....
....
....

3. What materials did you use to build your machine?

....
....
....
....

4. Was your machine successful in meeting the need? Why or why not?

....
....
....
....

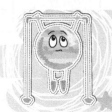
5. Were there any materials constraints on building your machine? Explain.

....

....

....

....

6. Were there any time constraints on building your machine? Explain.

....

....

....

....

7. Were there any cost constraints on building your machine? Explain.

....

....

....

....

 FITNESS PLANET ➡ Let's get some fitness in! Go to page 167 to try some fitness activities.

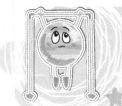

1. Chloe puts **243** books on bookshelves. Each shelf can hold **7** books. If Chloe fills each shelf with **7** books, how many books will be on the partially filled shelf?

2. What two numbers are factor pairs for **28**?

   A. 2 and 14
   B. 4 and 7
   C. 3 and 6

3. Rachel wrote the number **5**. If the rule is multiply by **3**, what is the third number of her pattern.

4. What is the value of the underlined digit? 1<u>5</u>2,183

   ....

5. Write the number using words: 129,340

   ....

   ....

6. Estimate the product. Round the second factor to the nearest ten, then multiply. 4 x 28

1. Estimate the sum by rounding each number to the nearest ten thousand then adding.

29,394 + 53,724 = ...

2. Charlie studied for his math test for **20** minutes. He studied for his Spanish test for **2** times the amount of minutes than he did for his spelling test. How many minutes did Charlie study for his Spanish test?

3. Is the number **67** prime or composite?

....

4. The red team is playing football against the purple team. Each touchdown is worth **6** points. The red team makes **3** touchdowns. The purple team makes **4** touchdowns. How many more points does the purple team have than the red team?

5. Which of the following numbers are a multiple of 6? 8, 36, 19

....

6. Estimate the difference by rounding each number to the nearest thousand then subtracting.

3,506 - 1,204 = ...

Read the following passage:

Snowed in!

The wind roared all night long as a winter storm passed through the area. Charlie woke up and looked outside: Everything was covered in a deep layer of pristine, white snow. Charlie ran downstairs.

"Morning, kiddo! School's canceled!" Dad said. "And my work even canceled today, too."

"Yes!" Charlie exclaimed. He gave his dad a big hug. He then looked out the window. He saw that the snow was so high that it covered part of the window glass!

"Dad, how much did it snow?" Charlie asked with wide eyes.

"Only two feet. But the wind blew the snow into large snow banks. Pretty much everyone on our block has a snow bank up to four feet high against their back door!" Dad explained. "I'm going to spend most of the day shoveling!"

"I'll help you, Dad," Charlie said.

"Thanks, buddy. I can always count on you," Dad said with a smile. "But first, let's eat some breakfast!"

Now answer the questions about the passage.

1. Using context clues, what is the meaning of the word "pristine"?

....

....

2. "Bank" is a homograph. Provide the definition of "bank" as it is used in the passage, and then provide two other possible meanings of the word.

meaning in this passage: ....

other meaning 1: ....

other meaning 2: ....

3. "Feet" is a homograph. Provide the definition of "feet" as it is used in the passage, and then provide another possible meaning of the word.

meaning in this passage: ....

other meaning: ....

4. What kind of relationship does Charlie have with his father? Use two pieces of textual evidence from the story to support your answer.

....

....

....

....

....

....

....

....

FITNESS PLANET → Let's get some fitness in! Go to page 167 to try some fitness activities.

FITNESS

1. Is the number 13 prime or composite?

....

2. What shape comes next?

3. Estimate the difference by rounding each number to the nearest ten then subtracting.

$394 - 157 = $ ☐

4. The shoe store sold 7 sandals over the weekend. It sold 5 more tennis shoes than sandals. Write an equation to show how many tennis shoes were sold.

5. Estimate the product. Round each factor to the nearest ten, then multiply.

$37 \times 19 = $ ☐

....

....

6. Add.

$$\begin{array}{r} 485 \\ + 159 \\ \hline \end{array}$$

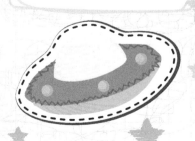

Personal budgets are plans that allocate income towards expenses, savings and debt repayment. Budgets allow people to effectively allocate their resources and plan for the future.

Directions: Read each question below. Write your answer in the space provided.

1. What are the important components of a budget?

....
....
....
....

2. Why is it important to have a budget?

....
....
....

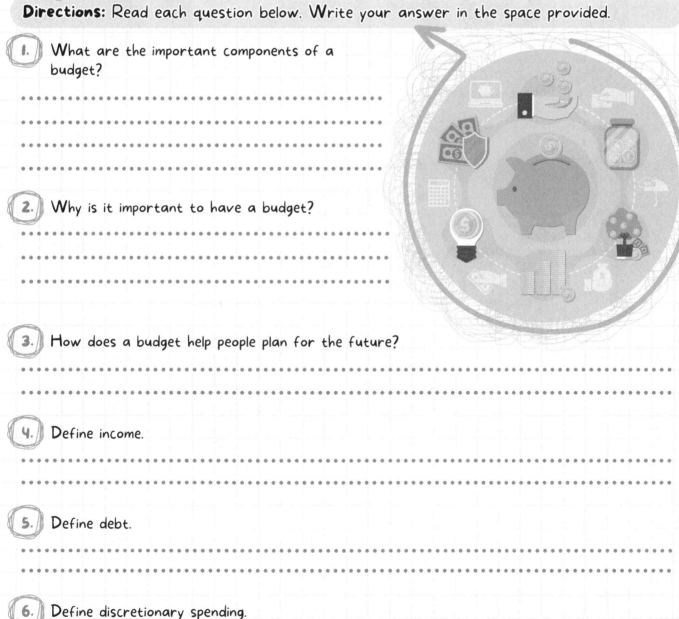

3. How does a budget help people plan for the future?

....
....

4. Define income.

....
....

5. Define debt.

....
....

6. Define discretionary spending.

....
....

Grade 4-5
WEEK 12

Let's finish up with:

* informational texts
* engineering
* editing
* commas and more!

BRAIN HUNTER

1. Three brothers receive 15 candies. They split them evenly between themselves. The letter c stands for the number of candies each child keeps. Which equation can you use to find c?

A. $15 - 3 = c$ B. $15 ÷ 3 = c$

2. Shea wrote a row of numbers with the following pattern: 4, 8, 12, 16, 20. What should the next number be?

....

3. What two numbers are factor pairs for 55?

A. 2 and 27   B. 5 and 11   C. 6 and 12

4. Amy has 4 children. She bought them a pack of 30 squishies and told them to share them equally. Complete the sentence. Each child gets .... pencils, with .... left over.

5. Write the number using words: 382

....

6. Subtract.

$$\begin{array}{r} 49{,}183 \\ -\ 24{,}409 \\ \hline \end{array}$$

FITNESS PLANET → Let's get some fitness in! Go to page 167 to try some fitness activities.

1. What is the value of the numeral 7 in the number 715,356

4. Is the number 21 prime or composite?

2. Fill in the missing digit.

$$
\begin{array}{r}
3,409 \\
+\ 2,\underline{}46 \\
\hline
5,855
\end{array}
$$

5. $12 \times 5 =$ ☐

3. Paul wants to buy two toys: one that costs $5.99 and another that costs $27.99. Paul has saved $20.00 so far. How much more money does he need to purchase both toys?

6. Which of the following numbers are a multiple of 5? 25, 17, 12

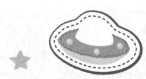

Read the following passage.

The Eiffel Tower

One of the most popular tourist attractions in the world is the Eiffel Tower. The Eiffel Tower was built to serve as the entrance to the World's Fair of 1889. Many engineers and designers submitted ideas for an entryway, and the winner of the contest was engineer Gustave Eiffel. The tower took two years to build. The tower is made mostly of wrought iron, and it weighs **22,000,000** pounds!

Originally, the tower was going to be temporary. After a period of twenty years, the city planned to take it down. However, people saw use in the tower once that period was over: The tower was used as a communications tower and an antenna was attached to the top. The tower now has hundreds of antennas at the top and wind turbines that produce green energy.

Millions of people visit the Eiffel Tower every year. Visitors can take an elevator to the top of the tower. The tower is almost **1,000** feet tall, so visitors can see for miles, enjoying the Parisian skyline.

Now, answer questions about the passage.

1. Name two facts about the Eiffel Tower.

....

....

....

2. How did the Eiffel Tower get its name?

....

3. Why did the city of Paris decide to keep the Eiffel tower?

....

....

....

4. In what year did engineers begin building the Eiffel Tower?

....

5. Give an example of a sentence that uses a comma after an introductory word.

....

6. "Contest" is a homograph. Provide the definition of "contest" as it is used in the passage, and then provide another possible meaning of the word.

meaning in this passage: ....

other meaning: ....

FITNESS PLANET → Let's get some fitness in! Go to page 167 to try some fitness activities.

FITNESS

Over the past few lessons, you explored engineering by designing and building a machine to assist with a need from your own life. Then, you answered questions about your machine and how well it worked.

Today, think about what you could do differently so that your machine is more successful in meeting the need. You should also think about the constraints you listed on materials, time and cost of building the original prototype.

. . . .

. . . .

. . . .

. . . .

. . . .

. . . .

. . . .

. . . .

. . . .

. . . .

. . . .

. . . .

. . . .

. . . .

. . . .

Sketch a prototype of your new and improved machine below.

1. Write the number using digits: fifty-three thousand five hundred seven.

2. Sean has 40 books. This is 4 times as many as Mark has. Write an equation to show how many books Mark has.

3. Use the model to find 2 x 15.

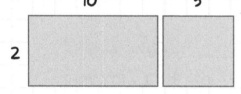

4. 800 is 10 times as much as ....

5. 120 x 30 = [ ]

6. A card has a length of 5 inches and a width of 4 inches. What is the area?

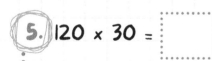

1.

$2\overline{)52}$

2.

$\dfrac{3}{4} = \dfrac{\square}{16}$

3. Is the number 88 prime or composite?

....

4.

$2\dfrac{3}{4} + 1\dfrac{2}{3} =$

5.

$\dfrac{1}{8} \; \square \; \dfrac{1}{5}$

6. 10 x 3 = 3 x 10 Which property of multiplication is shown?

A. associative

B. communicative

C. distributive

D. zero

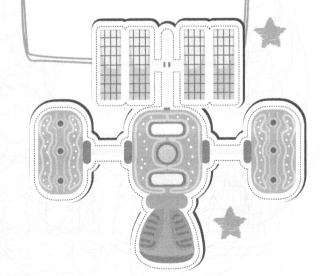

Whenever you finish a piece of writing, take a minute to edit it. Don't let errors ruin your great ideas! Look for errors such as the following:

* **Punctuation**
  * Did you punctuate each sentence with correct end punctuation?
  * Did you use commas when needed?
* **Capitalization**
  * Did you capitalize the first word of every sentence?
  * Did you capitalize proper nouns (names of specific people, places, things)?
* **Spelling: Did you spell all words correctly?**
* **Sentence Fluency and Repetitiveness**
  * Do your sentences flow smoothly?
  * Did you combine sentences when possible?
  * Did you avoid repeating the same word or idea over and over (think synonyms!)?

Read the following paragraph and make any editing corrections needed. There are at least twelve errors to correct.

I love baking! My favorite things to bake are cookies cakes and muffins. during the holidays I always bake sugar cookies. I bake heart-shaped cookies for valentine's day and pumpkin cookies for halloween. In addition I bake cakes for birthdays. My favorite cake to bake is chocolate cake. Finally I bake muffins every weekend My favorite flavors are bluberry and apple cinnamon muffins.

FITNESS PLANET → Let's get some fitness in! Go to page 167 to try some fitness activities.

FITNESS

Review the rules for using commas throughout this workbook. Add commas as needed in the following sentences.

1. She knew the answer already didn't she?

2. Because I was late for class I needed to stay after.

3. No I won't be able to help you after school.

4. My favorite activities are horseback riding sledding and baking.

5. Hey can you come over after school?

6. Well I should get ready to go now.

7. First I need to bring in the groceries.

8. After you finish your homework can you take the dog out for a walk?

9. Shhhh your father is resting.

10. Yes I will take the test on Monday.

11. Finally we will know the end of the story!

12. Shawn will come early won't he?

13. My favorite colors are pink light purple and blue.

14. Since you helped out your mother you can have extra time playing your game.

15. Sure I would be glad to come!

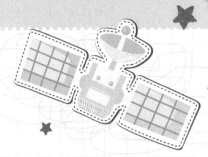

1. Use a rule to complete a number pattern. The rule is to multiply 6. 6, 36, ...

2. Romeo is collecting canned goods for the homeless. There are **22** people in his class and each person bring in **2** cans. He got **15** more cans from a business donation. Romeo thinks they have enough to give about **100** people a can. Does that sound about right?

A. Yes
B. No, that is much too high
C. No, that is much too low

3. Which number is a factor of 49?
2, 7, or 97

4. 9 x 1 + 9 x 0 = 9 x (1 + 0) Which property of multiplication is shown?

A. associative
B. communicative
C. distributive
D. zero

5.

$$7\overline{)916}$$

.... R ....

6. Choose **2** numbers from the table to complete the multiplication sentence.

3	4	5	6

.... x .... = 15

Personal budgets are plans that allocate income towards expenses, savings and debt repayment. Budgets allow people to effectively allocate their resources and plan for the future.

Directions: Create your own personal budget, including any income you have (allowance, money from birthdays, etc.), as well as expenses (snacks at school), savings and debts (money you owe your parents for new shoes).

Grade 4-5

FITNESS PLANET

FITNESS PLANET
Repeat these exercises 2 ROUNDS

exercises complex **one**

2 - **Lunges:** 4 times for each leg.
Note: Use your body weight or books as weight to do leg lunges.

1 - **Abs:** 7 times

3 - **Plank:** 9 sec.

4 - **Run:** 50m
Note: Run **25** meters to one side and **25** meters back to the starting position.

Please be aware of your environment and be safe at all times. If you cannot do an exercise, just try your best.

FITNESS

exercises complex **two**

1 - **High Plank:** 9 sec.

3 - **Waist Hooping:** 15 times. Note: if you do not have a hoop, pretend you have an imaginary hoop and rotate your hips 10 times.

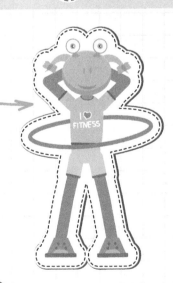

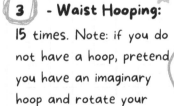

4 - **Abs:** 10 times

2 - **Chair:** 10 sec.
Note: sit on an imaginary chair, keep your back straight.

FITNESS PLANET
Repeat these exercises 2 ROUNDS

exercises complex three

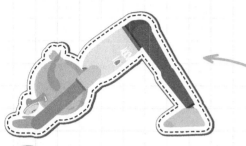

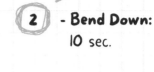

2 - **Bend Down:** 10 sec.

3 - **Chair:** 15 sec.

1 - **Down Dog:** 15 sec.

5 - **Shavasana:** as long as you can. Note: think of happy moments and relax your mind.

4 - **Child Pose:** 30 sec.

Please be aware of your environment and be safe at all times. If you cannot do an exercise, just try your best.

FITNESS

exercises complex four

2 - **Lunges:** 3 times for each leg.
Note: Use your body weight or books as weight to do leg lunges.

1 - **Bend forward:** 15 times.
Note: try to touch your feet. Make sure to keep your back straight and if needed you can bend your knees.

4 - **Abs:** 13 times

3 - **Plank:** 10 sec.

Grade 4-5

ANSWERS SHEET

ANSWER SHEET

Week 1

★ Week 1 ★ ?

★ Topic 1 ★ Interpret a multiplication equation as a comparison

★ Page 12 ★

1. 35	4. 8
2. 9	5. 8
3. 90	6. 6

★ Topic 2 ★ Multiply or divide to solve word problems involving multiplicative comparison

★ Page 13 ★

1. 18	4. 4
2. 7	5. 12
3. 60	6. 70

★ Topic 3 ★ Identifying word problem equations

★ Page 18 ★

1. 12 + 10 = 22	4. 30 x 4 = 120
2. 9 + 5 = 14	5. 12 = 3 x 4
3. 20 x 3 = 60	6. 35 = 5 x 7 or 35 / 5 = 7

★ Topic 4 ★ Divide 2-digit by 1-digit word problems

★ Page 19 ★

1. 3	4. 16
2. 1	5. $1
3. 1	

★ Topic 5 ★ Divide 3-digit by 1-digit word problems

★ Page 22 ★

1. 4	4. 3
2. 4	5. 4
3. 5	6. 3

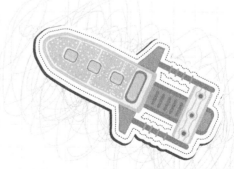

★ Week 1 ★ Reading

★ Topic 1 ★ Informational Text

★ Page 14-15 ★

1. Possible answer: The oceans contain 95% of the world's water, and water is essential to all life on earth.

2. Possible answer: The blue whale is over 80 feet long and is the world's largest animal.

ANSWER SHEET

3. An organism is an animal or a plant.
4. Possible answer: "they cannot be seen without a microscope"

5. Possible answer:

Arctic: smallest ocean

Atlantic Ocean: has a large underwater mountain range

Pacific Ocean: deepest part is here

★Week 1 ★ Writing

★ Topic 2 ★ **Parts of a Paragraph**

★ **Page 20** ★

1. Possible answer: I love to spend time outside in winter with my family.

2. Possible answer: It is easy to make pancakes.

★Week 1 ★ Reading

★ Topic 3 ★ **Fiction**

★ **Page 21** ★

1. Possible answer: Butterflies are beautiful after their transformation.
2. Delicate and light as a tiny feather.

3. "Purple blossom," "blaze orange beauty," and "wingless, green caterpillar"

★Week 1 ★ Science

★ Topic 1 ★ **Factors That Affect Motion**

★ **Page 17** ★

1. Pushing a stroller, pulling a wagon
2. A ball being rolled across the floor and slowing down when it moves from hardwood floors to carpet

3. A bike running into a fallen tree trunk and the person flying off
4. A person on roller skates gaining speed as they skate downhill

ANSWER SHEET

★ Week 1 ★ Social Studies

★ Topic 1 ★ Historic Native American Groups

★ Page 23 ★

All answers will vary.

Week 2

★ Week 2 ★ ?

★ Topic 1 ★ Multi-step word problems

★ Page 25 ★		★ Page 26 ★	
1. $176.80	4. 81	1. 13, 1	4. 7, 2
2. 40	5. $10.49	2. 7, $2	5. A. Yes
3. 4		3. 5, 2	

★ Topic 2 ★ Write variable equations to represent word problems

★ Page 31 ★

1. A. $10 - 4 = p$
2. A. $12 - p = 6$
3. B. $\dfrac{100}{10} = c$
4. B. $\dfrac{24}{3} = a$
5. A. $12 - 5 = c$
6. B. $\dfrac{50}{5} = t$

★ Topic 3 ★ Prime and composite numbers (1-20)

★ Page 32 ★

1. prime
2. composite
3. prime
4. prime
5. composite
6. composite

★ Topic 4 ★ Prime and composite numbers (1-100)

★ Page 35 ★

1. composite
2. prime
3. prime
4. composite
5. composite
6. prime

ANSWER SHEET

★ Week 2 ★ Language

★ Topic 1 ★ Conjunctions

★ Page 27 ★

1. I wanted to go outside after school, <u>but</u> my mom said I had to do my homework.
2. I forgot my homework, <u>so</u> I had to walk back to school.
3. Hopefully, a teacher <u>or</u> a custodian is there to let me into the school.
4. I have math <u>and</u> reading homework to complete tonight.

Possible answers:
1. I ate a snack and did my homework after school.
2. Ellie did her homework on time, but Maggie did not.
3. I finished my homework quickly, so I have time to go outside.
4. I might go on the swing set, or I might go for a bike ride.

★ Week 2 ★ Writing

★ Topic 2 ★ Parts of a Paragraph

★ Page 28 ★

1. I think cats are better pets than dogs.
2. Three

3. Possible answer: Finally, cats are trained in a litter box. They can be left alone for longer periods of time since they do not need to be let outside.
4. First, also, finally

★ Week 2 ★ Reading

★ Topic 3 ★ Information

★ Page 33-34 ★

1. The Apollo 11 is the first spacecraft to land on the moon (and the astronauts walked on the moon).
2. Possible answer:

July 16, 1969	July 20, 1969	July 24, 1969
Apollo 11 takes off	Apollo 11 lands on the moon	Apollo 11 returns

3. Possible answer: Parades were held in honor of the astronauts because no one had ever done what they did (walking on the moon).
4. Possible answer: No one had done what he and Buzz Aldrin accomplished. Although they only took a few steps on the moon, those steps were incredibly significant ("one giant leap").

ANSWER SHEET

5. Possible answers: There is no erosion on the moon, so the footprints don't get blown away by wind and water, as they would on Earth.
6. Possible answers: Other spacecraft had made it to space and back, but no one had yet landed on the moon. Neil Armstrong and Buzz Aldrin landed on the moon four days after takeoff.

★Week 2 ★ Science

★ Topic 1 ★ Speed and Energy

★ Page 29-30 ★

1. Answers will vary.

2. The bounce occurs due to the stored energy in the popper from turning it inside out.

★Week 2 ★ Social Studies

★ Topic 1 ★ Early Settlements

★ Page 36 ★

All answers will vary.

Week 3

★Week 3 ★ ?

★ Topic 1 ★ Multiples (up to 10)

★ Page 38 ★

1. 9
2. 36
3. 8
4. 16
5. 18
6. 30

★ Topic 2 ★ Identify factors

★ Page 39 ★

1. 4
2. 2
3. 9
4. 9
5. 1
6. 4

★ Topic 3 ★ Identify numbers to complete a product

★ Page 44 ★

1. 4, 6
2. 2, 8
3. 6, 9
4. 5, 9
5. 7, 9
6. 3, 9

ANSWER SHEET

★ **Topic 4** ★ **Find factor pairs**

★ **Page 45** ★

1. A. 5 and 15 and C. 3 and 25
2. B. 2 and 47
3. A. 2 and 42, B. 3 and 28, and C. 4 and 21
4. B. 2 and 33 and C. 6 and 11
5. B. 2 and 19
6. A. 1 and 11

★ **Topic 5** ★ **Generate patterns**

★ **Page 48** ★

1.
2.
3. ☆
4.
5.
6.

★ Week 3 ★ Reading

★ **Topic 1** ★ **Fiction**

★ **Page 40-41** ★

1. Katrina thinks her friends are angry with her.
2. Possible answers: "She had a hard time concentrating on the day's math lesson." and "She asked if they were mad as tears welled up in her eyes."
3. Katrina asked her friends directly if they were mad, and they explained why they acted the way the did.
4. Possible answer: It is better to communicate and ask questions rather than make assumptions. Katrina asked her friends and they had an explanation for their behavior. If Katrina wouldn't have asked, the conflict would not have been resolved.

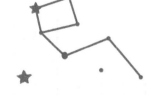

★ Week 3 ★ Language

★ **Topic 2** ★ **Commas**

★ **Page 46** ★

1. My mom asked me to walk the dog, take out the garbage, and unload the dishwasher.
2. Matthew ate chicken, mashed potatoes, and broccoli for dinner.
3. Grandma baked cookies and a cake for the party tonight.
4. Chantal, Gary, and Jorge will be at the concert.
5. I am not sure if Jonathan, Melissa, or Omar is coming, though.
6. The students visited the primates, farm animals, small mammals, and big cats sections of the zoo on their field trip.
7. Neither Jennifer or Carlos can come along on the field trip.
8. I took my dog for a walk, watered the flowers, and rolled in the garbage bins.

ANSWER SHEET

★ Week 3 ★ Writing

★ Topic 3 ★ Parts of a Paragraph

★ Page 47 ★

1. Possible answer: Winter is a great time for family fun.

2. Possible answer: Cats are an easy, relaxed pet to have.

★ Week 3 ★ Science

★ Topic 1 ★ Energy Conversions

★ Page 43 ★

All answers will vary.

★ Week 3 ★ Social Studies

★ Topic 1 ★ Early American Writers & Artists

★ Page 49 ★

All answers will vary.

Week 4

★ Week 4 ★ ?

★ Topic 1 ★ Use a rule to complete a number pattern

★ Page 51 ★

1. 60
2. 36
3. 1
4. 24
5. 54
6. 33

★ Topic 2 ★ Use a rule to complete a number pattern (word problems)

★ Page 52 ★

1. 28
2. 47
3.
4. 54
5. 5
6. 25, 125, 625

ANSWER SHEET

★ Topic 3 ★ Place value

★ Page 57 ★

1. A. 483, 667
2. 40,000
3. 800,000
4. C. 154, 322
5. 9,000
6. 600,000

★ Topic 4 ★ Place value (relationships)

★ Page 58 ★

1. 200
2. 60
3. 700
4. 300
5. 3,000
6. 6,000

★ Topic 5 ★ Place value (review)

★ Page 61 ★

1. 81,851
2. 62,563
3. hundreds
4. thousands
5. 9
6. 5

★Week 4 ★ Language

★ Topic 1 ★ Commas

★ Page 53 ★

1. When Sandra comes over, you can open that box of cookies.
2. Meanwhile, I will be walking home after school.
3. After you walk the dog, you can go over to Brian's house.
4. Furthermore, the principal will be contacting your parents this evening.
5. Because you were late for school, you need to stay after for ten minutes.
6. Since I already saw that movie, I decided to stay home.
7. First, you need to build the base.
8. Before you jump to conclusions, please listen to my explanation.

★Week 4 ★ Writing

★ Topic 2 ★ Writing an Opinion Paragraph

★ Page 54 ★

Answers will vary

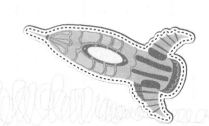

ANSWER SHEET

★Week 4 ★ Reading

★ Topic 3 ★ Informational Texts

★ Page 59-60 ★

1. The guide words for this page are "paper" and "party." They are useful because they tell you any word between "paper" and "party" alphabetically will be on this page.
2. Noun
3. It can be an adjective, noun, or verb.
4. Possible answer: parade, parallel, park, pardon
5. There are five different definitions.
6. This is the fourth definition.
7. Park: to sit down

★Week 4 ★ Science

★ Topic 1 ★ The Moon

★ Page 55-56 ★

All answers will vary.

★Week 4 ★ Social Studies

★ Topic 1 ★ Foundations of Government

★ Page 62 ★

1. Form a more perfect Union, establish justice, insure domestic tranquility, provide for the common defence, promote the general welfare and secure liberty
2. Answers will vary.
3. Answers will vary.

Week 5

★ Week 5 ★ ?

★ Topic 1 ★ Convert words to digits (up to 1,000)

★ Page 64 ★

1.	584	4.	304
2.	55	5.	662
3.	63	6.	960

★ Topic 3 ★ Convert words to digits (up to 100,000)

★ Page 70 ★

1.	734	4.	60,584
2.	66,322	5.	33,006
3.	24,110	6.	72,847

★ Topic 5 ★ Convert to digit and words (up to one million)

★ Page 74 ★

1. 534,698
2. 420,679
3. 997,002
4. two hundred fifty-three thousand five hundred three
5. one hundred twenty-five thousand seven hundred sixty-five
6. three hundred sixty-five thousand seven hundred

★ Topic 2 ★ Convert digits to words (up to 1,000)

★ Page 65 ★

1. fifty-two
2. six hundred twenty-three
3. four hundred nine
4. nine hundred seventy
5. twenty-four
6. six hundred ten

★ Topic 4 ★ Convert digits to words (up to 100,000)

★ Page 71 ★

1. ninety-three thousand five hundred sixty-four
2. forty-two thousand seven hundred
3. thirty thousand five hundred sixty-seven
4. twenty-four thousand five hundred nine
5. fourteen thousand six hundred seventy
6. thirty-six thousand six hundred seventy-eight

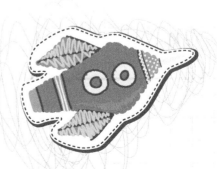

ANSWER SHEET

★Week 5 ★ Reading

★ Topic 1 ★ Fiction

★ Page 66 ★

1. Possible answers: the unusually dark setting, an unsigned letter

2. Answers will vary

★Week 5 ★ Writing

★ Topic 2 ★ Writing an Informational Paragraph

★ Page 67 ★

Answers will vary

★Week 5 ★ Reading

★ Topic 3 ★ Informational Texts

★ Page 72-73 ★

1. Cooking; possible title: Everyday Recipes
2. Chapter two
3. Chapter 5
4. "Cooking Tools and Tips"
5. "Nutrition Information"
6. Index

★Week 5 ★ Science

★ Topic 1 ★ Geological Processes

★ Page 68-69 ★

All answers will vary.

★Week 5 ★ Social Studies

★ Topic 1 ★ Key Ideas About Government

★ Page 75 ★

1. c
2. e
3. a
4. d
5. f
6. b

ANSWER SHEET

Week 6

★ Week 6 ★ ?

★ Topic 1 ★ Compare numbers (to one hundred thousand)

★ Page 77 ★

1. >	4. =
2. <	5. >
3. <	6. >

★ Topic 2 ★ Compare numbers (to one million)

★ Page 78 ★

1. >	4. <
2. <	5. <
3. >	6. =

★ Topic 3 ★ Place value word problems

★ Page 83 ★

1. 304,209	4. 450,624
2. 61,445	5. 33,029
3. 60,332	6. 672,900

★ Topic 4 ★ Rounding to millions place

★ Page 84 ★

1. 700	4. 260,000
2. 250	5. 300,000
3. 25,000	6. 975,000

★ Topic 5 ★ Estimate sums

★ Page 87 ★

1. 59,000	4. 6,000
2. 80,000	5. 130,000
3. 1,500	6. 470

★ Week 6 ★ Language

★ Topic 1 ★ Punctuating Titles

★ Page 79 ★

Longer titles can be underlined or italicized

1. We read a short story called "The Monkey's Paw" in language arts class.
2. Margaret finished reading *Out of my Mind* for her book report.
3. The teacher assigned us to read the chapter called "Caring for Your Pet" over the weekend.
4. *People* and *Time* are two popular magazines.
5. My favorite poem is "Sick" from the book *Where the Sidewalk Ends*.
6. I read the article "American Goldfinch" from the website *National Geographic Kids*.

ANSWER SHEET

★Week 6 ★ Language

★ Topic 2 ★ Parts of Words

★ Page 80 ★

1. I like to read <u>non</u>fiction books.
2. She had to <u>re</u>type her essay.
3. Callie <u>mis</u>behaved in language arts class.
4. The two wires became <u>dis</u>connected.
5. We took a <u>pre</u>test in math yesterday.

1. not tied → untied
2. heat before → preheat
3. play again → replay
4. not agree → disagree
5. not toxic → nontoxic

★Week 6 ★ Reading

★ Topic 3 ★ Fiction

★ Page 85-86 ★

1. Morning on the planet Narg
2. Any three of the following: three moons, a red sun, sleeping orbs, pods, spaceships in the sky, communicating via hologram
3. Possible answer: people eat breakfast, there is only one sun

4. Sleeping orb: bedroom
   Pod: house
5. Possible answer: "I am surprised that Narg's leader is not worried about this ship" is an example of foreshadowing because it shows that this ship is likely not a bad thing, as the protagonist thought it would be.

★Week 6 ★ Science

★ Topic 1 ★ How Humans Impact the Environment

★ Page 81-82 ★

All answers will vary.

★Week 6 ★ Social Studies

★ Topic 1 ★ Contemporary Issues of Civic Responsibility

★ Page 88 ★

All answers will vary.

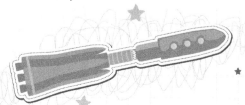

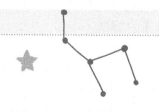

ANSWER SHEET

Week 7

★ Week 7 ★

★ Topic 1 ★ Estimate differences

★ Page 90 ★

1. 300
2. 300
3. 2,000
4. 90,000
5. 700
6. 12,000

★ Topic 2 ★ Estimate sums and differences (word problems)

★ Page 91 ★

1. 30,000
2. 1,310
3. 145,000
4. 60
5. 600
6. 11,000

★ Topic 3 ★ Estimate products (multiply by 1 digit)

★ Page 96 ★

1. 80
2. 750
3. 240
4. 600
5. 600
6. 7,200

★ Topic 4 ★ Estimate products (multiply by 2 digits)

★ Page 97 ★

1. 600
2. 1,400
3. 3,600
4. 4,500
5. 7,200
6. 25,000

★ Topic 5 ★ Estimate and divide by 1-digit numbers

★ Page 100 ★

1. 130
2. 40
3. 92
4. 110
5. 60
6. 23

ANSWER SHEET

★Week 7 ★ Reading

★ Topic 1 ★ Fiction

★ Page 92-93 ★

1. Possible answer: A family plans a surprise pet adoption; that could happen in real life today. A young girl longs for a pet; that could also happen today.
2. The quotation "her mother replied with a mischievous smile" shows that her mother is up to something unusual.
3. Possible answer: "Warm kitchen" (feeling), "wonderful aromas" (smell), "a quiet mewing" (hearing)
4. Mischievous: playful or teasing
   Aromas: smells or odors
5. Possible answer: Hola, sweet child.

★Week 7 ★ Language

★ Topic 2 ★ Parts of Words

★ Page 98 ★

1. The witness described the event.
2. The plant produces food using photosynthesis.
3. My sister suffers from arachnophobia.
4. Photograph means "light writing." (both "photo" and "graph" are roots)
5. We measured the perimeter of the circle.

1. Barometer
2. Biography
3. Spectator
4. Claustrophobia
5. Prescriptions

★Week 7 ★ Writing

★ Topic 3 ★ Figurative Language

★ Page 99 ★

Answers will vary

ANSWER SHEET

★Week 7 ★ Science

★ Topic 1 ★ Inherited Traits

★ Page 94 ★

1. Answers will vary.
2. Answers will vary.
3. Answers will vary.
4. Plants and animals can inherit traits from their parents, just as humans do.

★Week 7 ★ Social Studies

★ Topic 1 ★ Native American and Colonial Settlements

★ Page 101 ★

1. Native Americans and colonists tended to settle near sources of food and water, along transportation routes or near other natural resources or sources of power.
2. Answers will vary.
3. The Native Americans and colonists settled in these areas so that they would have ample food, water, natural resources for making and building things, power and be able to easily transport or move along transportation routes.

Week 8

★Week 8 ★

★ Topic 1 ★ Add multi-digit numbers

★ Page 103 ★

1. 684
2. 403
3. 5,835
4. 63,169
5. 60,701
6. 6,219

★ Topic 2 ★ Subtract multi-digit numbers

★ Page 104 ★

1. 14,967
2. 129
3. 616
4. 1,022
5. 8,526
6. 2,243

ANSWER SHEET

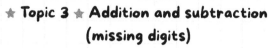

★ Topic 3 ★ Addition and subtraction (missing digits)

★ Page 109 ★

1. 5	4. 2
2. 3	5. 7
3. 7	6. 0

★ Topic 4 ★ Multiplication (facts to 12)

★ Page 110 ★

1. 60	4. 33
2. 56	5. 42
3. 48	6. 63

★ Topic 5 ★ Multiplication (area model)

★ Page 113 ★

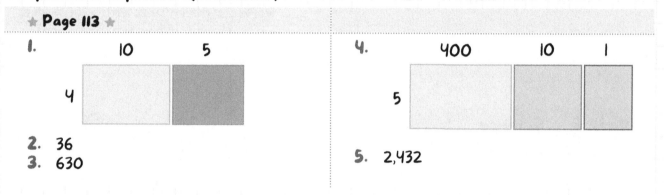

2. 36
3. 630

5. 2,432

★Week 8 ★ Language

★ Topic 1 ★ Parts of Words

★ Page 105 ★

1. The train conduct<u>or</u> rang the bell.
2. The movie was enjoy<u>able</u>.
3. My mom is very help<u>ful</u> with my homework.
4. I quick<u>ly</u> ran to my class.
5. She specializes in neur<u>ology</u>.

1. lovingly
2. biology
3. painful
4. visible
5. boxer

★Week 8 ★ Reading

★ Topic 2 ★ Fiction

★ Page 106 ★

1. "The sun shines like a gemstone." This simile means that the sun is sparkling brightly.
2. Possible answer: "children play in the sapphire water." This metaphor shows that the water is a rich color and also most likely sparkling.
3. "The sun shines like a gemstone in the sky, Happily watching over the children below." The sun cannot be happy as it is an object. Giving it an emotion is personification.

ANSWER SHEET

★ Page 111-112 ★

1. Possible answer:

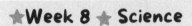

Mouth ——— Body that is 95% water

——— Tentacles that sting

2. Possible answer: Jellyfish have no eyes. Jellyfish do not have a brain.
3. Invertebrate: lacking a backbone
   Resilient: able to handle any conditions
   Currents: water moving in a direction
4. Possible answer: Jellyfish survive easily no matter where they are. When the world's temperatures fall, jellyfish are not bothered. When the world heats up, jellyfish are fine.

★ Week 8 ★ Science

★ Topic 1 ★ Animal Adaptations

★ Page 108 ★

All answers will vary.

★ Week 8 ★ Social Studies

★ Topic 1 ★ Drainage Basins

★ Page 114 ★

1.
1. Northwest
2. California, Nevada
3. Colorado Basin
4. Missouri Basin
5. Arkansas Red Basin
6. West Gulf
7. Lower Mississippi
8. North Central
9. Ohio
10. Southeast
11. Middle Atlantic
12. Northeast

2. Drainage basins are important sources of nutrients, sediments and pollutants from the water flowing through the drainage and river. As they are transported toward the outlet of the drainage basin, ecological processes are affected and other living things receive the things they need to survive. They are also a source of coal and fuels.

ANSWER SHEET

Week 9

★ Week 9 ★

★ Topic 1 ★ Multiply numbers ending in zero

★ Page 116 ★

1. 400
2. 7,200
3. 5,200
4. 250
5. 720
6. 7,200

★ Topic 2 ★ Properties of multiplication and division

★ Page 117 ★

1. B. communicative
2. D. zero
3. C. distributive
4. B. 1 x 8 = 8
5. 7
6. 9 x 9 = 81

★ Topic 3 ★ Division

★ Page 122 ★

1. 8
2. 11
3. 282
4. 403
5. 6 R 1
6. 182 R 1

★ Topic 4 ★ Equivalent fractions

★ Page 123 ★

1. 10
2. 9
3. 50
4. 24
5. 15
6. 20

★ Topic 5 ★ Fractions

★ Page 126 ★

1. <
2. >
3. >
4. >
5. >
6. <

ANSWER SHEET

★Week 9 ★ Language

★ Topic 1 ★ Commas

> ★ Page 118 ★

1. Gee, I didn't realize that she was feeling left out.
2. Uh-oh, I think we forgot to buy dog food.
3. Shhhh, the baby is sleeping.
4. Aw, that was so kind of you to help out.
5. Well, she didn't have to be rude about it.

★Week 9 ★ Reading

★ Topic 2 ★ Informational Text

> ★ Page 119 ★

1. Possible answer: Tsunamis are dangerous storms that develop quickly from events deep in the ocean.
2. Tsunamis form when a volcano erupts or there is an earthquake in the ocean.
3. Possible answer: "they can uproot trees"

★Week 9 ★ Writing

★ Topic 3 ★ Combining Sentences

> ★ Page 125★

Answers will vary

★Week 9 ★ Science

★ Topic 1 ★ Ecosystems

> ★ Page 121 ★

All answers will vary.

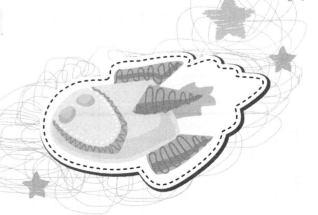

ANSWER SHEET

★ Week 9 ★ Social Studies

★ Topic 1 ★ Physical Regions of the United States

★ Page 127 ★

1. Pacific Coast-Westernmost region: includes the high mountain ranges of the Sierra Nevada and Cascades
2. Intermountain region: area between the mountains on the Pacific Coast and the Rocky Mountains, includes deserts, mountains, plateaus and canyons
3. Rocky Mountain region: includes the highest mountain range in North America
4. Interior Plains region: includes fertile soil for farming and grasslands, includes the Great Plains and Central Plains
5. Appalachian Mountain region: stretches from Canada to Georgia, lower and less rugged mountain range than others
6. Canadian Shield region: extends from Canada into Michigan, Wisconsin and Minnesota
7. Coastal Plains region: includes the Atlantic Coast and Gulf Plains, includes flat, lowland areas
8. Hawaiian Islands region: wet, tropical climate and dense tropical rainforest

  Week 10

★ Week 10 ★

★ Topic 1 ★ Add and subtract fractions

★ Page 129 ★

1. $\frac{5}{10}$

2. $\frac{1}{6}$

3. $\frac{1}{3}$

4. $4\frac{1}{8}$

5. $1\frac{1}{8}$

6. $1\frac{1}{2}$

★ Topic 2 ★ Multiply fractions

★ Page 130 ★

1. 1
2. 2
3. 5
4. 3
5. 1
6. 2

ANSWER SHEET

★ Topic 3 ★ Decimals

★ Page 135 ★

1. .3
2. .09
3. .5
4. .68
5. $\frac{4}{10}$
6. $\frac{6}{10}$

★ Topic 5 ★ Geometric measurement

★ Page 139 ★

1. acute
2. obtuse
3. obtuse
4. right
5. acute
6. right

★ Topic 4 ★ Perimeter and area

★ Page 136 ★

1. 44 cm
2. 120 feet
3. 35 square inches
4. 40 square inches
5. 15 inches
6. 8 feet

★Week 10 ★ Language

★ Topic 1 ★ Synonyms and Antonyms

★ Page 131 ★

1. Synonym
2. Antonym
3. Synonym
4. Synonym
5. Antonym

★Week 10 ★ Writing

★ Topic 2 ★ Personal Narrative

★ Page 132 ★

All answers will vary.

★Week 10 ★ Reading

★ Topic 3 ★ Fiction

★ Page 138 ★

1. Possible answers: Many people did immigrate from Ireland to Boston in the 1800s. Many people moved west in the hopes of a better life during Westward Expansion.
2. Possible answers: Free land, and cities were crowded
3. People could have a large piece of land (160 acres) for free if they lived on it for five years.
4. Possible answer: A married couple immigrated from Irealnd to Boston. They had several children and worked hard. They decided to move west to become farmers.

ANSWER SHEET

★ Week 10 ★ Science

★ Topic 1 ★ Exploring Engineering

★ Page 133-134 ★

All answers will vary.

★ Week 10 ★ Social Studies

★ Topic 1 ★ Important Places in the United States

★ Page 140 ★

All answers identified on map or globe.

Week 11

★ Week 11 ★ Mixed Review

★ Topic 1 ★ Review

★ Page 142 ★

1. 16
2. 5
3. A. 10 − 3 = s
4. 3
5.

★ Page 143 ★

1. 1,000
2. 24,208
3. 6, 8
4. <
5. 84
6. acute

★ Page 148 ★

1. 5
2. A. and B.
3. 45
4. 50,000
5. one hundred twenty-nine thousand three hundred forty
6. 120

ANSWER SHEET

★ Page 149 ★

1. 80,000
2. 40 minutes
3. prime
4. 6
5. 36
6. 3,000

★ Page 152 ★

1. prime
2.
3. 230
4. 7 + 5
5. 800
6. 644

★Week 11 ★ Language

★ Topic 1 ★ Homographs

★ Page 144 ★

Answers will vary

★ Topic 2 ★ Commas

★ Page 145 ★

1. She was late again, wasn't she?
2. The dog doesn't bite, does it?
3. No, my dog is very friendly and never bites anyone.
4. Sure, you can come along on the trip.
5. It's going to rain again, isn't it.
6. Yes, it does look like it is going to rain.

★Week 11 ★ Reading

★ Topic 3 ★ Fiction

★ Page 150-151 ★

1. Clean, spotless, fresh
2. Meaning in this passage: a mound of snow
   Possible answers:
   other meaning 1: a place to store money
   other meaning 2: the land alongside a river
3. Meaning in this passage: a unit of measure equalling twelve inches
   other meaning: the lower part of the leg on which a person or animal walks
4. Possible answer: Charlie and his father have a close relationship. The reader sees this when Charlie gives his dad "a big hug" as soon as he gets up. Also, the father says that he "can always count on" Charlie, signaling they are there for each other.

ANSWER SHEET

★Week 11 ★ Science

★ Topic 1 ★ **Exploring Engineering**

★ **Page 146-147** ★

All answers will vary.

★Week 11 ★ Social Studies

★ Topic 1 ★ **Personal Budgeting**

★ **Page 153** ★

1. Amount of income, breakdown of debts to be paid, discretionary spending needs, amount of savings needed
2. It is important to have a budget so that you are not spending more than what you make and are able to pay all debts while still putting money aside for savings.
3. A budget helps people plan for the future by allocating a certain amount of money for savings. Budgets can be tailored based on decisions made about how to spend or save money.
4. Income is the money coming in from any employment.
5. Debts are the money owed (i.e. rent/mortgage, car, utility payments)
6. Discretionary spending is the money needed for items that are wants rather than needs (i.e. clothing, entertainment)

Week 12

★Week 12 ★ Mixed Review

★ Topic 1 ★ **Topic: Review**

★ **Page 155** ★

1. B.
2. 24
3. B.
4. 7, 2
5. three hundred eighty-two
6. 24,774

★ **Page 156** ★

1. 700,000
2. 4
3. $13.98
4. composite
5. 60
6. 25

ANSWER SHEET

1. 53,507
2. 40 ÷ 4
3. 30
4. 80
5. 3,600
6. 20 square inches

1. 26
2. 12
3. composite
4. $4\frac{5}{12}$
5. <
6. B.

1. 216
2. C.
3. 7
4. C.
5. 130 R 6
6. 3, 5

★ Week 12 ★ Reading

★ Topic 1 ★ Informational Text

★ Page 157-158 ★

1. Possible answers: the tower is almost 1,000 feet tall. Millions of people visit the tower every year.
2. It is named after the engineer who designed it, Gustave Eiffel.
3. They realized the tower was useful for antennas.
4. They began building the tower in 1887.
5. Originally, the tower was going to be temporary.
6. meaning in this passage: a competition
   (Possible answer)
   other meaning: a dispute

★ Week 12 ★ Writing

★ Topic 2 ★ Editing

★ Page 163 ★

Answers will vary depending on how students combined sentences and what synonyms they used to avoid repetition.

I love baking! My favorite things to bake are cookies, cakes, and muffins. During the holidays, I always make sugar cookies, such as heart-shaped cookies for Valentine's Day and pumpkin cookies for Halloween. In addition, I bake cakes for birthdays. My favorite cake is chocolate cake. Finally, I make muffins every weekend. My favorite flavors are blueberry and apple cinnamon muffins.

ANSWER SHEET

★Week 12 ★ Language

★ Topic 3 ★ Commas

★ Page 164 ★

1. She knew the answer already, didn't she?
2. Because I was late for class, I needed to stay after.
3. No, I won't be able to help you after school.
4. My favorite activities are horseback riding, sledding, and baking.
5. Hey, can you come over after school?
6. Well, I should get ready to go now.
7. First, I need to bring in the groceries.
8. After you finish your homework, can you take the dog out for a walk?
9. Shhhh, your father is resting.
10. Yes, I will take the test on Monday.
11. Finally, we will know the end of the story!
12. Shawn will come early, won't he?
13. My favorite colors are pink, light purple, and blue.
14. Since you helped out your mother, you can have extra time playing your game.
15. Sure, I would be glad to come!

★Week 12 ★ Science

★ Topic 1 ★ Exploring Engineering

★ Page 159-160 ★

All answers will vary.

★Week 12 ★ Social Studies

★ Topic 1 ★ Personal Budgeting

★ Page 166 ★

All answers will vary.